W9-AML-640

365 Science Activities

Written by **Minna Lacey,
Dr. Lisa Gillespie**
and **Lucy Bowman**

Designed by
**Anna Gould, Hannah Ahmed,
Matthew Preston, Zoe Wray,
Holly Lamont** and **Karen Tomlins**

Expert advice:
Dr. Steven Chapman

Illustrated by
**Alex Walker, Giulia Olivares,
Francesca Carabelli**
and **Binny Talib**

About this book

This book is full of science activities and experiments you can do at home. Each one has simple step-by-step instructions showing you what to do, and a straightforward explanation of the science involved.

Each activity is numbered.

These boxes explain what's going on in each activity and the science behind it.

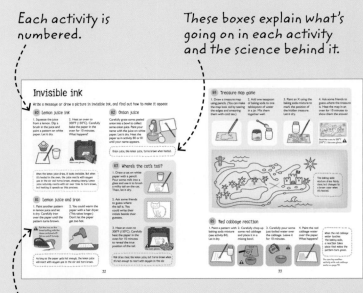

Warning symbols show if you need to take extra care.

Don't worry if things don't always turn out as you expect — some of the most important discoveries in science were made by accident.

The activities use everyday items, such as plastic bottles and cardboard boxes. You'll also need some craft items, such as paper, pens and string.

There are all kinds of activities, from experimenting with static electricity to making invisible ink.

Science safety ⚠️

Activities are meant to be done with the guidance of an adult, and some activities involve using heat sources or household chemicals and require an adult's help. Always handle hot things, sharp items, and chemicals carefully, and never put anything in your mouth unless the instructions tell you to.

Contents

Experiment with paper planes on page 6.

Discover how to make your own goo and slime on page 49.

Compare parachute designs on page 126.

Test for acids using cabbage water on page 90.

Learn about wildlife on page 56.

Usborne Quicklinks

For links to websites where you can find online science activities, go to the Usborne Quicklinks website at **www.usborne.com/quicklinks** and type in the keywords '365 science activities.' Please read our internet safety guidelines at the Usborne Quicklinks website.

Find out how to dye leaves on page 125.

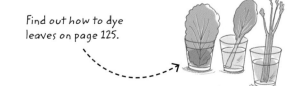

Dye, oil and water

Find out how some substances mix and others don't, and discover the amazing effects you can create by adding food dye or water-based ink to oil and water.

1 Make dye drops

Pour some vegetable oil into a tall glass. Add a few drops of food dye and watch what happens.

Food dye

Vegetable oil

Each dye drop forms a tight bead shape because dye does not mix with oil, so the drop can't spread out.

2 Staying in shape

Push the drops of dye gently down into the oil with a spoon and see what happens.

The dye drops sink in the oil because food dye is denser than oil (see the "Density" box on page 5). The drops keep their shape because the liquids don't mix.

3 Exploding dye drops

Fill a tall glass with water, add some vegetable oil and let it settle. Then, add a few drops of food dye and watch what happens.

Oil

Nudge the drops with a spoon to make them sink more quickly.

Water

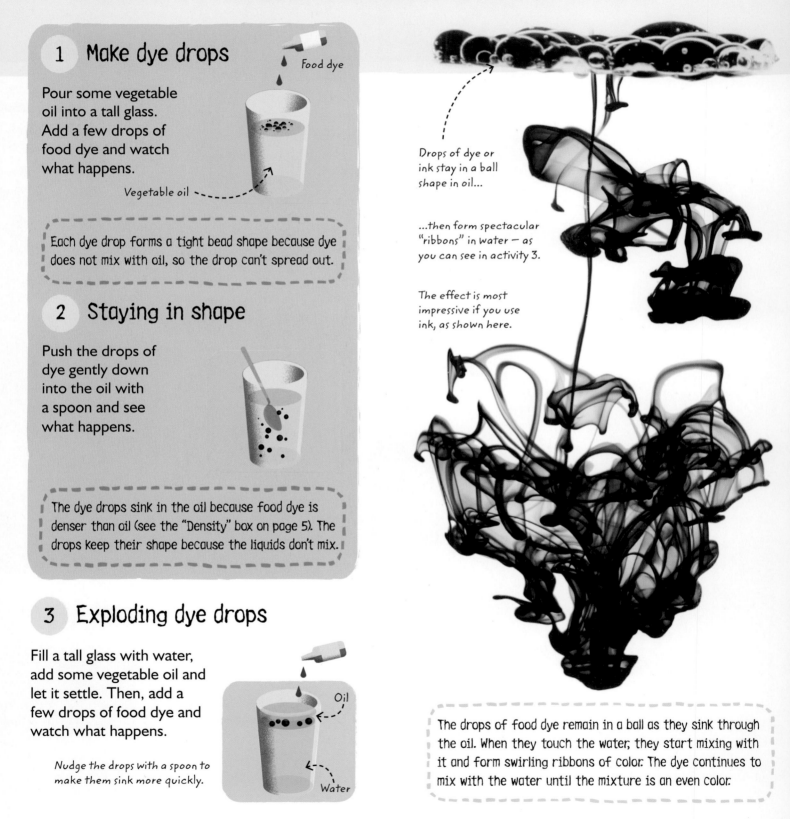

Drops of dye or ink stay in a ball shape in oil...

...then form spectacular "ribbons" in water – as you can see in activity 3.

The effect is most impressive if you use ink, as shown here.

The drops of food dye remain in a ball as they sink through the oil. When they touch the water, they start mixing with it and form swirling ribbons of color. The dye continues to mix with the water until the mixture is an even color.

4

Density

Everything is made of tiny particles. Density is about how heavy and how spread out the particles in a substance are. If two liquids of different densities are mixed, the less dense one floats on the denser one. For example, oil floats on water.

4 Add dishwashing liquid

Add some food dye to half a glass of water. Pour vegetable oil into the glass and let it settle. Then, pour a few drops of dishwashing liquid into the glass and watch what happens.

Keep adding dishwashing liquid drops to see the effect for longer.

Oil

Dishwashing liquid

Oil drops

Food dye and water

Drops of dishwashing liquid sink to the bottom of the glass, pushing drops of oil down beneath them. But oil is less dense than dishwashing liquid and water, so the oil drops escape and rise back to float on the surface again.

5 Mix it up

Repeat the last experiment, but this time stir everything up well with a spoon. Notice what happens this time.

Dishwashing liquid is attracted to both water and oil, which allows them to mix together. The mixture eventually becomes evenly colored as the dye spreads all the way through it.

6 Dye and milk

1. Pour some milk into a saucer and add some drops of food dye or colored ink.

2. Dip a cotton swab in dishwashing liquid and place it in the middle of the milk. What happens?

Remove the swab when the milk and food dye start to mix together.

This pattern was created with just one color of dye.

The dye doesn't mix well with milk. But when dishwashing liquid is added, the dishwashing liquid is attracted to both the milk and the dye, and allows them to mix together more quickly.

Paper planes

Make some paper planes and find out what makes them fly.

7 Make a paper plane

1. Fold a rectangle of paper in half, following the direction of the arrow.

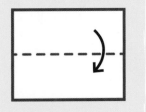

2. Fold the bottom right-hand corner up to the top edge.

3. Fold the new flap up to the top edge, like this.

4. Then, fold it up once more.

5. Turn the paper over...

6. ...then repeat steps 2, 3 and 4.

7. Open out the wings a little and throw the plane.

8 Aiming up and down

Try aiming your plane slightly up or down as you throw it. How does it fly?

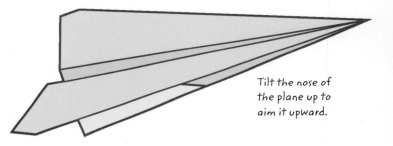

Tilt the nose of the plane up to aim it upward.

When you throw a paper plane forward, the air flows around its wings and creates lift. If you change the angle you throw the plane, the airflow changes, helping the plane fly farther or making it fall to the ground faster.

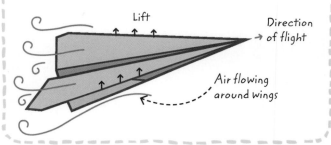

Lift

Direction of flight

Air flowing around wings

9 Add a paper clip

Attach a paper clip to the nose of your plane. Does it change the way the plane glides?

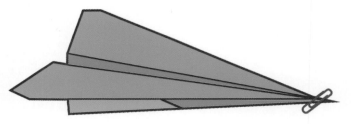

The extra weight of the paper clip gives the plane more forward force, helping it to fly farther.

10 Fold the wing tips

Fold the tips of your plane's wings up and throw the plane. Then try pointing them down instead. Does it fly differently?

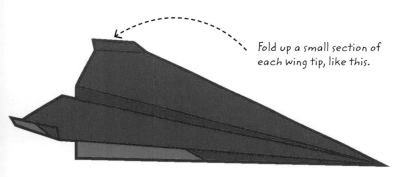

Fold up a small section of each wing tip, like this.

11 Experiment with steering

Point one wing tip up and one wing tip down. Which way does the plane fly? Now try it the other way.

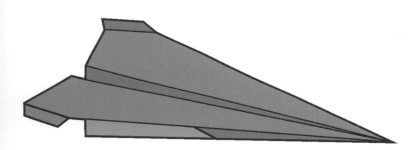

The wing tips change the way the air catches the wings. When the wing tips point up, the plane tilts up. When they point down, it tilts down. And if one points up and one points down, the plane will swoop sideways.

Folding the left wing tip up and the right wing tip down steers the plane left.

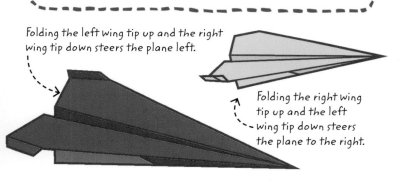

Folding the right wing tip up and the left wing tip down steers the plane to the right.

12 Make a glider

1. Fold a rectangle of paper in half, length-ways and width-ways. Then, unfold it again.

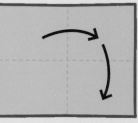

2. Fold the top part down, like this.

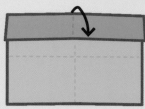

3. Fold in both upper corners so that they meet in the middle.

4. Fold the top down again, like this.

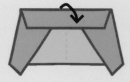

5. Turn the plane over and fold it in half.

6. Fold back both wings, like this.

This glider has broad wings. The bigger the surface area of the wings, the more air pushes up on them. This means the plane can glide farther than the planes from the earlier activities, whose wings have a smaller surface area. Does yours? Do some tests.

Paper, wood and water

Try these experiments to see how different types of paper soak up water.

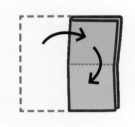  

Don't cut these two sides.

1. Fold a square of paper in half. Then, fold it in half again, like this.

2. Draw a petal shape on the square and cut it out. Open the flower shape.

3. Fold in each petal, like this. Pour some water into a bowl and place the flower on the water.

4. Watch the petals slowly open as the paper starts to absorb the water.

The paper is made of tiny fibers pressed together. As the fibers absorb (soak up) the water, they expand and push the flower petals open.

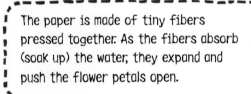 

You could give your flowers different numbers of petals and see if it makes a difference.

14 Paper towel flower

Repeat activity 13 using a paper towel to make your flower.

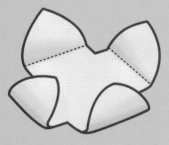

A paper towel is made of very thin layers of paper. It absorbs water so fast that the flower sinks before it has a chance to open.

8

15 Card stock flower

Try activity 13 again with a piece of card stock.
How long does the flower take to open?

*You could try flowers
with different shaped petals.
Does the shape affect the time
the flower takes to open?*

> Card stock is thicker than paper because it contains more
> fibers. It takes longer than paper to absorb water, so the
> flower takes longer to open. The more card stock there is in
> a petal's shape, the longer it takes for the petals to open.

16 Glass to glass

1. Roll up a paper towel and put one end in an empty glass. Half-fill another glass with water and tint it with a couple of drops of food dye.

2. Place the other end of the paper towel in the glass of water and leave it for a few hours. What happens to the water?

> The paper towel absorbs the water until it is soaked
> through and the water starts to leak out into the empty
> glass. If you wait long enough, both glasses will end up
> with roughly the same amount of water.

17 Make a wooden star

1. Bend five wooden toothpicks into 'v' shapes without breaking them in two. Arrange them like this on a plate. Add a few drops of water to the middle.

2. Watch what happens as the toothpicks absorb the water.

> Toothpicks are made of wood fibers. As each
> toothpick absorbs water, it expands and pushes
> its "arms" apart until they rest against their
> neighbor. This makes a neat star shape.

Foaming fizz

Find out what baking soda does when you add it to different liquids.

18 Hot water

Carefully pour some just-boiled water into a heatproof bowl. Stir in a heaped teaspoon of baking soda. What happens?

19 Cold water

Pour some cold water into a bowl, then add a heaped teaspoon of baking soda. Watch closely to see if anything happens.

Baking soda fizzes gently when it mixes with hot water because the heat starts a change that gives off bubbles of carbon dioxide gas. (This is why baking powder – which contains baking soda – is used to make cakes. The oven's heat makes the wet baking soda produce carbon dioxide gas, which bubbles up inside the cake mixture and tries to escape, making the mixture rise.) Cold water has no effect.

20 Lemon juice or vinegar

1. Put a glass bowl on top of a tray. Half-fill the bowl with lemon juice or clear vinegar.

2. Sprinkle a heaped teaspoon of baking soda over the liquid, then watch what happens next.

Vinegar and lemon juice are acids*. When you mix them with baking soda, the ingredients change very vigorously. This produces lots of bubbles of carbon dioxide gas, which makes the mixture froth and fizz.

21 Foaming fizz

1. Repeat step 1 of activity 20, then stir a good squeeze of dishwashing liquid into the lemon juice or vinegar.

2. Add a few drops of food dye, then sprinkle a heaped teaspoon of baking soda over the liquid. What happens?

Adding dishwashing liquid makes the mixture foam up more because it traps the bubbles of gas from the reaction. The food dye helps you to see more clearly what is happening.

*You can find out more about acids on pages 90-91.

22 Funky froth

Make the fizz from activity 21 in a few different shaped containers to see how the foam flows differently out of the tops.

23 Fizzing sherbet

Buy a tub of sherbet and dab some on your tongue. Can you feel it fizzing?

Sherbet usually contains a mixture of baking soda and citric acid powder. When the sherbet gets wet in your mouth, the ingredients start to change, making bubbles of carbon dioxide gas that you can feel tingling on your tongue.

Try varying the quantities of the ingredients to see how much foam you get.

Balancing mobiles

Create some different mobiles and discover how to make them balance.

A mobile hangs evenly when objects on each side of the hanging point are balanced. To adjust the balance, move the objects closer to or farther away from the hanging point.

24 Ruler mobile

Make two different-sized balls from craft clay or poster tack. Tie a length of string around each one and hang one from each end of a ruler. Hang the ruler at its center. Can you make the ruler balance by moving just the bigger ball?

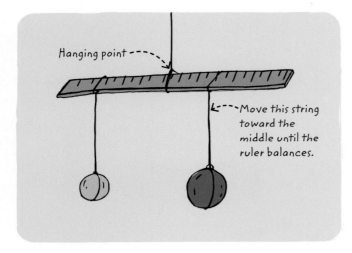

Hanging point

Move this string toward the middle until the ruler balances.

25 Make a cross shape

Arrange two sticks in a cross shape and use poster tack to hold them in place. Tie a length of string around the middle of the cross, then hang paper shapes from the sticks. Can you make it balance?

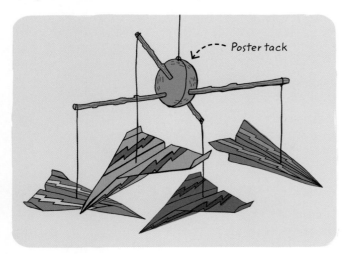

Poster tack

26 Paper clip mobile

Attach some paper shapes to the bottom of several paper clip chains. Hang the chains from straws. Use more paper clip chains to hang the straws and make a mobile. Can you make it all balance? How many levels can you add?

You can use a pencil to make holes to hang paper shapes.

27 Coat hanger mobile

Tie some spoons, forks and other kitchen utensils to a coat hanger and hang it up. Can you adjust the distance between the strings to make the hanger level?

12

28 Make a twig mobile

1. Draw and cut out four birds from card stock. (You can decorate them if you like.) Tie a length of string to each.

Make a hole with a hole punch.

2. Tie some string to the middle of a twig and hang a bird from each side. Attach two more birds to another twig.

3. Hang the twigs from each side of a third twig, then hold or hang up your mobile. Can you make it balance?

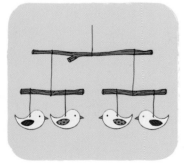

Hanging point

This side is heavier, so the string needs to be close to the hanging point in order to balance the mobile.

This side is lighter, so the string needs to be farther away from the hanging point.

You don't have to make bird shapes for your mobile — you can use any set of identical shapes.

29 Another branch

Make two more birds and attach them to another twig. Add this twig to the mobile. Can you still make the mobile balance?

The balance depends on the weight of the objects and their distance from the hanging point. You can adjust the balance by moving heavier objects closer to the hanging point and lighter objects farther away from it. Objects that weigh the same will balance at an equal distance from the hanging point.

Testing friction

When things rub together you get a force called friction, which slows them down. You can make a marble run to test this effect.

(30) Make a marble run

1. Place a shoebox on its side, on a piece of cardboard. Draw around it three times to make three ramps.

2. Extend the lines to make the ramps slightly longer than the shoebox. Cut them out.

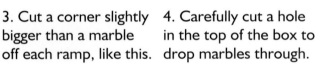

3. Cut a corner slightly bigger than a marble off each ramp, like this.

4. Carefully cut a hole in the top of the box to drop marbles through.

5. Position the ramps in the box so they slope from side to side, like this. Adjust the ramps so they tilt down slightly at the back, too.

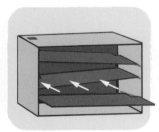

Use poster tack to attach popsicle sticks underneath the ramps to support them.

6. Drop a marble through the hole and watch it roll down.

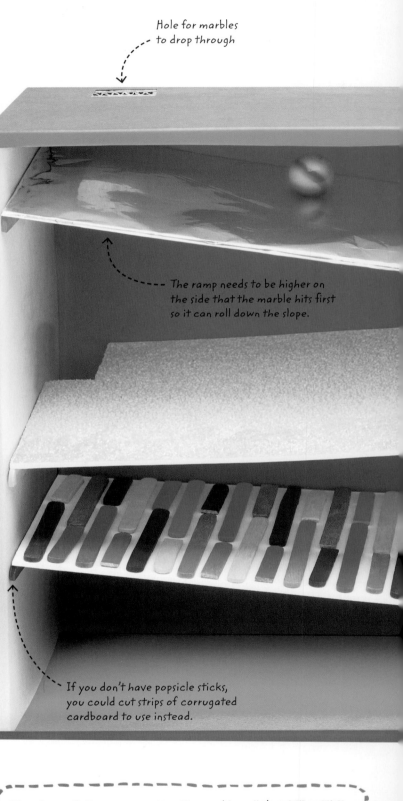

Hole for marbles to drop through

The ramp needs to be higher on the side that the marble hits first so it can roll down the slope.

If you don't have popsicle sticks, you could cut strips of corrugated cardboard to use instead.

The slope of the ramps makes the marble roll downhill until it reaches the bottom. As it rolls, friction is created between the marble and the ramp, which slows the marble's speed.

31 Smooth foil

Try wrapping a ramp in a new sheet of aluminum foil to make a smooth surface. How does it affect the speed of the marble?

The smooth surface of the foil reduces friction between the ramp and the marble. This helps the marble roll more quickly.

The ramp should tilt slightly toward the back of the box, so the marble falls down this hole to the next ramp.

32 Sandpaper

Glue sandpaper or sand onto a ramp to make a rough surface. What effect does it have on the marble's speed?

The rough surface increases friction, making the marble roll more slowly.

33 Popsicle sticks

Glue popsicle sticks or dry spaghetti along a ramp to make an even rougher surface. What happens to the speed of the marble now?

A very rough, bumpy surface increases friction even more and slows down the marble farther still.

34 More ideas

Test out the effects of different ramp surfaces using materials such as crumpled tissue paper, crumpled foil, bubble wrap, fabric or giftwrap.

35 Time it

Make three smooth ramps, then replace them with three rough ramps. Time how long it takes for the marble to reach the bottom each time. How much difference is there?

Optical illusions

Try out these optical illusions to learn more about your eyes and brain, and how they can be tricked.

 36 ## Darker or lighter?

Which end of this green bar looks darker?

Cover everything except the bar. How does it look now?

> The bar is all the same shade of green. But when it is next to a lighter green, it looks darker; and when it is next to a darker green, it looks lighter. Your brain judges the color of the bar depending on what is next to it.

37 ## What do you see?

A vase... ...or two faces?

> Both pictures exist at the same time, but your eyes can only focus on one at once. When you see the two blue faces, you can't properly see the vase; when you see the vase, the faces just become a blue background.

38 ## Which is longer?

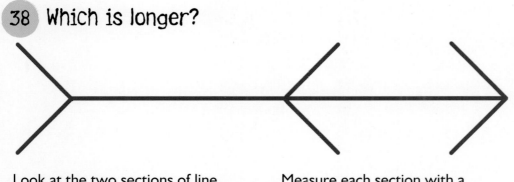

Look at the two sections of line. Which line *seems* longer?

Measure each section with a ruler. Which line *is* longer?

> Both sections are the same length, but the section with extra lines sloping outward looks longer, and the section with inward-sloping lines looks shorter. Your brain judges things by what is around them and is tricked by the extra lines sloping in different directions.

39 Strange squares

Do these squares have curved sides, or straight sides? Use a ruler to check your answer.

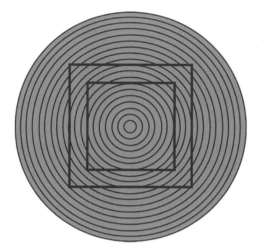

The squares have straight sides, but the curved lines behind the squares trick your brain into thinking that the sides of the squares must also be curved.

40 Phantom dots

Move your eyes over this grid. Can you see dots between the corners of the squares? Now stare at one dot. What happens?

When you move your eyes over this grid, your brain tries to join up the images by merging parts of the grid together. That's why you start to see ghostly dots. When your eyes stop moving and stare at one dot, it disappears.

41 Missing shapes

1. Look at this picture. Can you see a triangle in the middle?

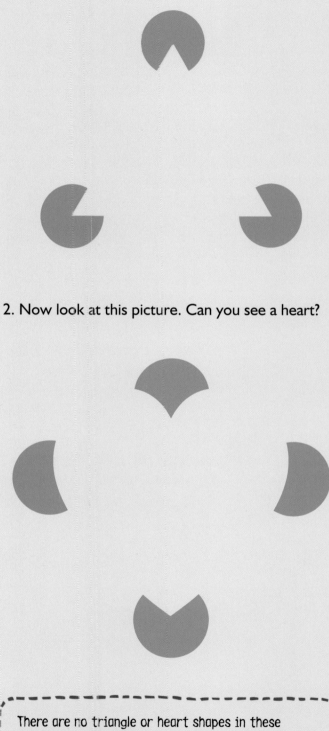

2. Now look at this picture. Can you see a heart?

There are no triangle or heart shapes in these pictures. Your brain sees the edges of where the shapes could go, and imagines the rest.

Melting ice

Try these experiments to learn about how ice melts.

42 Melting race

Place three ice cubes on a plate. Sprinkle one with sugar, one with salt and one with pepper. Which melts the fastest?

The temperature at which ice changes to water is called its melting point. (This is also the temperature at which water changes into ice, when it is called its freezing point.) Adding things to ice can lower the melting point. Salt lowers it the most, so the salty ice cube should melt the fastest. Pepper lowers it the least, so the peppery cube should melt the slowest.

The melting point of ice is 32°F (0°C). When ice reaches this temperature it changes to water.

43 See how it works

1. Fill a plastic box with water and leave it in the freezer overnight.

2. Tip the ice onto a big tray and sprinkle a thin layer of salt over the top.

You may have to wait for the ice to melt a little to get it out of the box.

3. Add some drops of ink on top. What happens to the ink?

You could use food dye instead of ink.

Salt lowers the melting point. The ice that the salt touches melts faster than the rest of the ice, creating cracks and rivulets. The ink flows into the gaps and helps you see what's happening.

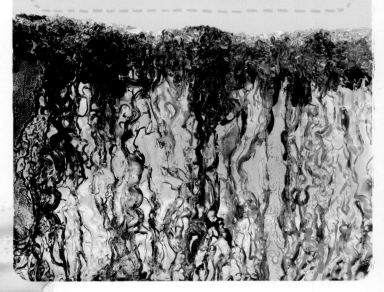

44 Ice in the light

Make a thin ice block by pouring a small amount of water into a round plastic box. Sprinkle the ice with salt and ink (or food dye), then hold it up to the light to see the colors glow.

The inky ice is thin enough for light to shine through it, like stained glass.

45 Cutting ice

1. Take a piece of strong nylon thread, about 8in (20cm) long and tie it around the middle of two pencils, like this.

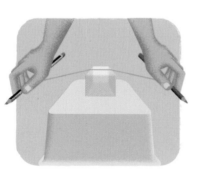

2. Put an ice cube on a plastic box and place the middle of the thread on top. Push down on the pencils, so the thread presses firmly on the ice.

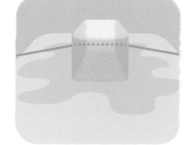

3. Watch the thread as you press down. It should move gradually down through the ice. See if you can cut the ice cube in two.

The pressure of the thread lowers the melting point. This helps the ice melt, allowing the thread to slip down into the ice. The water above the thread is still cold enough to refreeze, so the ice cube remains in one piece.

46 Picking up ice

1. Place an ice cube on a plate. Dip a piece of string in water and lay one end on top of the ice cube.

2. Sprinkle half a teaspoon of salt over the ice cube. Count to twenty, then lift up the string. What happens?

The salt makes the ice start to melt, and the string moves down into the ice cube slightly. But the ice inside is still cold enough to freeze the damp string onto the cube, so you can lift it with the string.

Flying Kites

Learn how to make kites from plastic or paper, and discover what makes them fly.

47 Plastic bag kite

Tie a long piece of string to the handles of a thin plastic bag. Hold the end of the string and run along with the bag behind you.

> The bag's light weight makes it easy for the wind to lift the bag into the air.

48 Paper bag kite

Cut the bottom off a paper grocery bag. Then, cut out some streamers from tissue paper and tape them around the bottom.

Tie string to the handles, then run along, pulling the paper-bag kite behind you.

> The air blows through and around the bag, creating a force called lift. This makes the bag flutter up in the air.

49 Diamond-shaped kite

Place the cross-piece about a third of the way down.

1. Make two wooden skewers into a cross and attach them with poster tack. Tie some string around the middle to secure it.

Tape

2. Place the frame on a plastic bag. Draw a diamond shape around the frame and cut it out. Tape the shape to the frame.

Make a hole here.

3. Turn your kite over. Use a sharp pencil to make a hole in the plastic where the sticks cross.

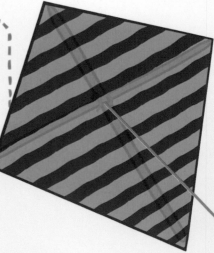

4. Thread the end of a ball of string through the hole. Tie it to the frame. Take your kite outside and test it.

> When wind blows over a kite and you pull on the string, it creates a force called lift. This force makes the kite rise in the air.

There are some tips about flying kites on the opposite page.

20

How to make your kite fly

To fly a kite, hold the string and run into the wind (so the wind is blowing in your face), pulling the kite behind you. Or ask someone to throw the kite up in the air, while you run.

Lift

You need an open area with a light wind to fly a kite.

50 Long-tailed kite

Tape together strips of newspaper or tissue paper to make a long paper tail. Then, tape the tail to the bottom of the kite from activity 49. Does it change how the kite flies?

Adding a tail makes the kite fly more smoothly. It gives it extra weight and helps balance the kite, so it doesn't twist and turn as much in the wind.

Strips of newspaper taped together

Strips of tissue paper

Try making a diamond kite as in activity 49, but using paper. Kites can be made of any material, as long as it's light, and strong enough not to tear in the wind.

Walking on water

Make bugs from card stock that stand on water, and discover how this works.

51 Make a water bug

1. Fold a piece of card stock in half. Then, draw a bug shape with three legs and feet, like this. Make sure the top of the bug touches the fold in the card stock.

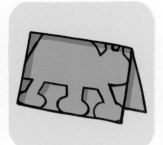

2. Cut neatly around the shape, being careful not to cut along the fold. Then, fold out the bug's feet so the shape stands up.

Don't cut here.

3. Fill a dish with water and gently place the bug on top, so all its feet touch the surface at once. Can you make it balance on the water?

Make sure the feet sit flat.

The surface of water is like a thin, stretchy skin, held together by a force called surface tension. Light objects can balance on this skin – as long as they don't break through it.

You can make your bug any shape or size...

...but the bigger the bug, the bigger its feet need to be for it to balance on the water.

52 Big-foot bug

Repeat activity 51 to make another bug, but this time with bigger feet. Is it easier to make it stand on the water?

It should be easier to balance the big-footed bug on water, because bigger feet spread the bug's weight more evenly over the water's surface.

53 Heavy bug

Repeat activity 51, but this time tape a coin onto each side of the bug's back. Can you still make the bug stand on the water?

Tape a coin on each side.

The bug with the coins is too heavy, so it breaks the water's skin and sinks.

54 Greasy feet

Make another bug and smear butter or margarine under its feet. Place it on the water. Does it work better?

Grease repels water, which makes it easier for the bug to stay on the surface. Many real water bugs have oily feet, too.

55 Float a needle

Drop a needle into a bowl of water and watch it fall to the bottom. Now dry the needle, place it on a piece of tissue and lay it carefully on the water. What happens?

Press gently on the tissue with a pencil to help it sink.

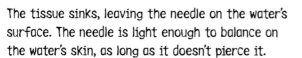

The tissue sinks, leaving the needle on the water's surface. The needle is light enough to balance on the water's skin, as long as it doesn't pierce it.

57 Sit or sink

Sprinkle some pepper over a bowl of water and watch to see if it floats or sinks. Then, stir the water. What happens?

At first, the pepper sits on the surface. Stirring the water breaks the water's skin, so the pepper then sinks.

56 Soapy water

Repeat activity 55, so the needle is lying on the water. Then, add a few drops of dishwashing liquid. What happens this time?

The dishwashing liquid breaks up the water's skin, and the needle sinks.

58 Moving pepper

Sprinkle some pepper over a bowl of water. Then, add a few drops of dishwashing liquid. What happens?

The dishwashing liquid breaks up the water's skin, so the pepper is pulled to where the skin is still in place.

Melting

Try these melting experiments to turn various solids into liquids.

You could experiment with lots of different colors of wax crayons and see if dark colors melt faster than light colors.

59 Crayon art

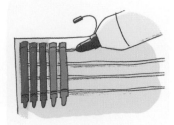

⚠️ Ask an adult to watch you heat the crayons.

1. Using craft glue, glue a row of wax crayons to the top of a piece of white cardboard.

2. Prop the cardboard against a wall, with the crayons on top and plenty of newspaper behind and underneath.

3. Move a hot hair dryer over the crayons to melt the wax on the cardboard. Leave the wax to cool.

Wax is solid at room temperature – around 68°F (20°C). But like all solids, when it gets hot enough, it melts, turning into liquid. When it is cool enough, it becomes solid once again.

Marshmallows

1. Squeeze a marshmallow between your fingers to find out what it feels like. Squeeze gently at first, then more firmly. Then, put it on a small plate.

2. Put the plate in a warm place, such as on a sunny windowsill or under a bright lamp. Wait for a few minutes, then squeeze the marshmallow again. How does it feel now?

> Marshmallows are light and fluffy, and melt easily. As your marshmallow gets warm, it will start to soften. If it gets really warm, it will melt and become liquid.

61 Black and white paper

1. Put a piece of black paper and a piece of white paper under a bright lamp.

2. Place an ice cube on each piece of paper. Which ice cube melts first?

Place the lamp in the middle of the two pieces of paper.

> The ice cube on the black paper should melt first. This is because black absorbs light and heat from the lamp, which keeps more heat in the paper, helping to melt the ice more quickly. White, however, reflects light and heat.

62 Milk chocolate

1. Place a square of milk chocolate on a plate in the sunshine.

2. Place a second square under a bright lamp.

3. Put another square of chocolate in your mouth. Which of the three melts the fastest?

> Milk chocolate melts fastest in your mouth, as your body temperature heats it up quickly. It will probably melt slowest under a lamp, unless the bulb is very hot.

63 Chocolate melting race

1. Suck a square of milk chocolate (no chewing) and time how long it takes to melt.

2. Now do the same with a square of dark chocolate. Which melts in the fastest time?

> Milk chocolate has more fast-melting fat in it than dark chocolate. Dark chocolate also contains more cocoa powder, which makes it melt more slowly. You can't taste chocolate until it melts, so you should taste the milk chocolate faster than you taste the dark chocolate.

How plants grow

Most plants start out as seeds, but they need the right conditions to make them grow. Find out what makes seeds sprout and grow into strong, healthy plants.

 Leaves

64 Grow some sprouting beans

You can use any whole, dried beans.

1. Fold two paper towels and put them in a plastic sandwich bag. Pour enough water on the paper towels to make them damp all over.

2. Place four beans in the middle of the bag. They should stick slightly to the paper. Seal the bag and tape it to a piece of cardboard.

3. Prop the cardboard on a sunny windowsill. Leave it there for a week, adding water to the bag every few days to keep the paper damp. What happens?

Stalk

Beans are a kind of seed. If you give them warmth and water, they will begin to sprout into baby plants called seedlings. You should see tiny green shoots grow up toward the light, and white stringy roots grow down. But for these seedlings to keep growing into plants, they also need to be planted in soil.

Shoot

Bean

Bean shell

Roots

Soil

Bean shell

Bean

Roots

65 Light and warmth

1. Take the bean seedlings from activity 64. Fill two flower pots with compost. Poke two holes in each, then gently place a seedling in each hole.

2. Place one pot on a sunny windowsill and the other in a cool, dark room. Water both pots every few days to keep the soil damp. What can you see after a week?

Stand the pots on saucers.

The pot on the windowsill should get plenty of light and warmth. This will help the seedlings to grow, so you should soon see bigger green shoots. The other seedlings won't grow much because they will lack light and warmth.

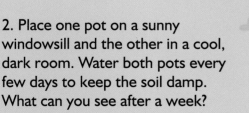

66 Thirsty seeds

1. Put some cotton balls in two yogurt cartons on a warm and sunny windowsill. Sprinkle some cress seeds over each.

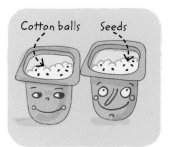

Cotton balls   Seeds

2. Add water to one of the cartons to dampen the cotton balls. Keep them damp over the next week. Leave the other carton dry. What happens?

The seeds on the damp cotton balls will sprout, but the others will not because they don't have the water they need.

67 Growing shoots

Carefully cut the top off a carrot. Place it on a saucer and add water. Cover the carrot top with a glass. Replace the water over the next few days. What happens?

Roots help plants to soak up water. The carrot is really a root (the root of a carrot plant) and will soak up the water, helping the stalk to grow some new leaves.

68 Making roots

Carefully cut off the bottom of a carrot. Stick four toothpicks around the top. Balance the toothpicks on the top of a glass so the carrot hangs in the middle. Fill the glass with water. What happens over the next few days?

The carrot in the water should sprout extra white thready roots to help it soak up the water.

Stalk and leaves

Carrot

Tiny thready roots

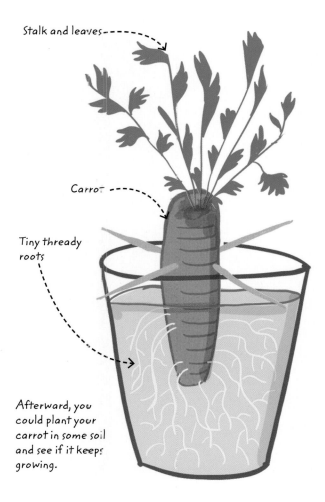

Afterward, you could plant your carrot in some soil and see if it keeps growing.

Yeast

Find out what yeast is and what it can do.

69 Make a frothy mixture

1. Mix two teaspoons of dried yeast with 8½ ounces (235ml) of warm water in a bowl. Add a teaspoon of sugar.

2. Stir the ingredients slowly for a minute or two. Then, let the mixture stand and watch what happens.

You may have to wait 10 minutes before seeing a result.

Yeast is a type of living thing known as a fungus. When it is mixed with warm water and sugar, yeast feeds on the sugar and gives off a gas called carbon dioxide. Bubbles of this gas form in the liquid, creating a thick layer of froth on the surface as they try to escape.

70 Inflate a balloon

1. Add two teaspoons of dried yeast and two teaspoons of sugar to half a glass of warm water. Then, stir it well.

2. Pour the mixture into a bottle. Stretch a balloon over the top of the bottle and leave it in a warm place. What happens?

The yeast reacts with the warm water and sugar to give off carbon dioxide gas. The gas expands to fill up the bottle, then starts to inflate the balloon, too.

71 Yeast and flour

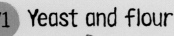

1. Take two plastic bottles and add one teaspoon of dried yeast, one teaspoon of sugar and half a glass of warm water to each one.

2. Add two tablespoons of flour to one bottle. Swirl both bottles around to mix the contents.

3. Place a balloon over the top of each bottle and leave the bottles in a warm place for 10 minutes. Then, compare the balloons.

Tip: Stretch out the balloon a couple of times before you put it over the bottle.

The balloon on the bottle with flour added to the mixture inflates more than the balloon on the bottle containing just warm water, yeast and sugar. This happens because the yeast feeds on the flour as well as on the sugar, which creates more gas.

72 Make a loaf of bread

Wash your hands before this activity.

1. Place 2½ cups (250g) of flour, a pinch of salt and two teaspoons of olive oil in a mixing bowl. Add a bowl of frothy yeast mixture (see activity 69).

2. Mix all the ingredients together with your fingers to make a dough. Keep squeezing the dough until it forms a firm ball.

3. Sprinkle some flour on a work surface. Then, stretch, fold and press the dough on the floured surface for 10 minutes.

4. Return the dough to the bowl and cover it with food wrap. Leave it in a warm place for an hour, until the dough puffs up.

The dough should double in size.

⚠ Wear oven gloves.

5. Press and fold the dough on a floured surface again, but more gently this time.

6. Make the dough into a loaf shape and place it on a greased baking tray.

7. Leave it in a warm place for 30 minutes to rise. Heat up the oven to 450°F (230°C).

8. Put your bread into the oven for 20-25 minutes, or until golden brown.

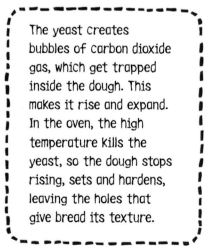
The yeast creates bubbles of carbon dioxide gas, which get trapped inside the dough. This makes it rise and expand. In the oven, the high temperature kills the yeast, so the dough stops rising, sets and hardens, leaving the holes that give bread its texture.

If you cut a slice of baked bread, you can see tiny holes in it. These are made by the bubbles of carbon dioxide gas.

Yeast is used all over the world as an ingredient to make dough rise when baking bread.

Salt crystals

Explore how salt crystals react with water by making patterns in wet paint.

73 Salt

1. Brush some watery paint over a piece of thick paper.

2. Lightly sprinkle some salt over the paint. Then, leave it to dry.

Add the salt while the paint is wet.

3. When the paint is completely dry, use a dry sponge to brush off any loose salt.

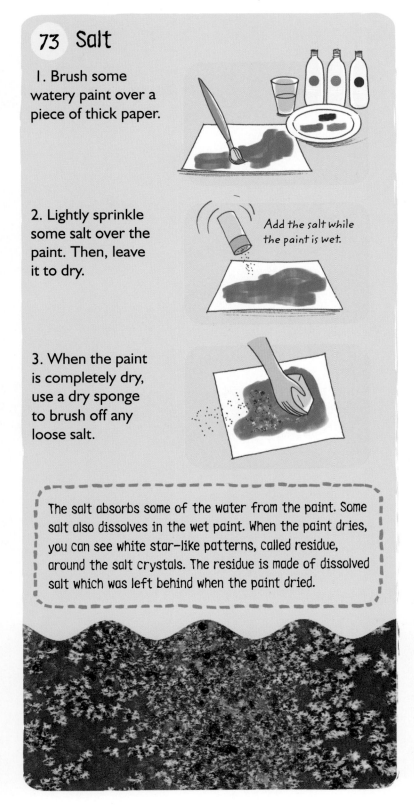

The salt absorbs some of the water from the paint. Some salt also dissolves in the wet paint. When the paint dries, you can see white star-like patterns, called residue, around the salt crystals. The residue is made of dissolved salt which was left behind when the paint dried.

74 Salt and paint mix

Mix a tablespoon of salt with watery paint. Brush the salty paint over thick paper and wait for it to dry.

This creates a more even, speckly effect. You can see white residue where the salty paint has dried.

75 Thick paint

Brush thick paint on thick paper, and sprinkle salt over it. What happens this time?

If the paint is very thick, the salt can't soak up as much water and doesn't dissolve, so the effect is less noticeable.

76 Large salt crystals

Sprinkle a pinch of coarse salt with large crystals onto a patch of watery paint. How does the pattern compare with those from 73, 74 and 75?

Large salt crystals don't dissolve as easily in the wet paint. But they leave bigger white patterns of residue.

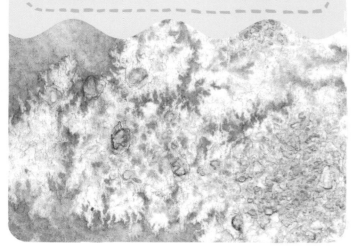

77 Dip in water

Pick up a large salt crystal with tweezers, dip it in water, then drop it onto a patch of watery paint. Do this several times.

The large salt crystals start to dissolve when dipped in water. More of the salt then dissolves in the wet paint, leaving larger white residue patterns.

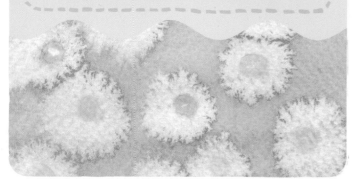

78 Crushed salt

Crush some large salt crystals with a rolling pin. Then, sprinkle the pieces over some wet paint.

When crushed into different sized pieces, the salt creates a varied effect. You can see different sized white patches of salt residue.

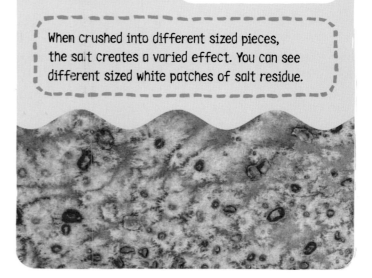

79 Sugar

Sprinkle some sugar over wet paint. Let it dry, then brush it off with a dry sponge. Does it have a similar effect to salt?

Although sugar and salt crystals look similar, sugar absorbs more water than salt and more of it dissolves. When it has dried, it is harder to brush off because dissolved sugar sticks like glue. It also leaves less white residue.

Invisible ink

Write a message or draw a picture in invisible ink, and find out how to make it appear.

 80 Lemon juice ink

1. Squeeze the juice from a lemon. Dip a paintbrush in the juice and paint a pattern on white paper. Let it dry.

2. Heat an oven to 300°F (150°C). Carefully bake the paper in the oven for 10 minutes. What happens?

Wear oven gloves.

When the lemon juice dries, it looks invisible. But when it's heated in the oven, the juice reacts with oxygen gas in the air and turns brown, showing clearly. Lemon juice naturally reacts with air over time to turn brown, but heating it speeds up this process.

81 Lemon juice and iron

1. Paint another pattern in lemon juice and let it dry. Carefully iron over the paper until the pattern turns brown.

2. You could warm the paper with a hair dryer, to reveal the pattern. This takes longer. (Don't let the paper get too hot.)

Put the iron on the lowest setting, with the steam switched off. Ask an adult to help.

As long as the paper gets hot enough, the lemon juice will react with oxygen gas in the air and turn brown.

82 Onion juice

Carefully grate some peeled onion into a bowl to collect some onion juice. Paint your name with the juice on white paper. Let it dry. Heat the paper as in activity 80 or 81 until your name appears.

Onion juice, like lemon juice, turns brown when heated.

83 Where's the cat's tail?

1. Draw a cat on white paper with a pencil. Pour some milk into a glass and use it to brush a milky tail on the cat. Then, let it dry.

2. Ask some friends to guess where the tail is. You could write their initials beside their guesses.

3. Heat an oven to 300°F (150°C). Carefully heat the paper in the oven for 10 minutes to reveal the true position of the tail.

Use oven gloves.

Milk dries clear, like lemon juice, but turns brown when it's hot enough to react with oxygen in the air.

84 Treasure map game

1. Draw a treasure map using pencils. (You can make the map look old by tearing the edges and smearing them with cold tea.)

2. Add one teaspoon of baking soda to one tablespoon of water in a jar. Mix them together well.

3. Paint an X using the baking soda mixture to mark the position of the hidden treasure. Let it dry.

4. Ask some friends to guess where the treasure is. Heat the map in an oven for 10 minutes to show them the answer.

Heat the oven to 300°F (150°C). Use oven gloves. ⚠

The baking soda mixture dries fairly clear, but changes to a brown color when it's heated.

85 Red cabbage reaction

1. Paint a pattern with baking soda mixture (see activity 84). Let it dry.

2. Carefully chop up some red cabbage and place it in a mixing bowl.

3. Carefully pour some just-boiled water over the cabbage. Leave it for 10 minutes.

4. Paint the red cabbage water over the paper. What happens?

When the red cabbage water touches the baking soda, a reaction takes place that makes the pattern turn green or blue.

You can try another activity with red cabbage water on page 90.

Sound experiments

Find out how to make some simple musical instruments, and experiment with the sounds they make.

86 Make an echo box

1. Stretch a rubber band between your thumb and first finger. Use your other hand to pluck it. Notice how loud the sound is.

2. Cut a hole in the lid of a shoe box. Stretch a rubber band across the hole and pluck it. Is this sound louder?

When you pluck the band, it vibrates and makes the air vibrate too, creating a sound. When the band is stretched over the box, the sound echoes around the box, making it louder.

87 Make an instrument

1. Find some thick and thin rubber bands the same length as each other. Stretch them over the shoe box, in order of thickness.

2. Hold the box steady with one hand and pluck the bands with the other. What types of sounds do you hear?

Box from activity 86

What is sound?

Sounds are caused by tiny movements, called vibrations, that travel through the air and the things around us. When these vibrations reach our ears, we hear them as sounds.

You could glue pieces of thick cardboard under the bands like this to make the sounds last longer. (This happens because more of the rubber band is not touching the box so is free to vibrate.)

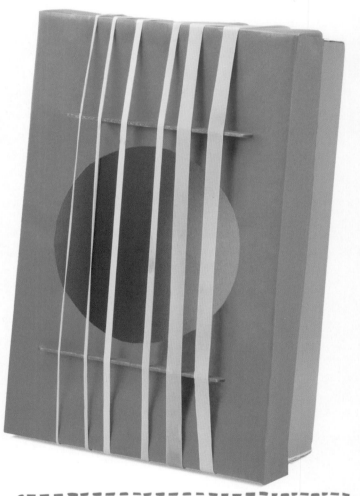

Different types of bands make different sounds. Thick bands vibrate more slowly and make deeper sounds; thin bands vibrate more quickly, making higher sounds. The harder you pluck the string, the bigger the vibrations are and the louder the sound.

88 Loud and soft

Put a handful of rice or dried beans in a clean jar. Screw on the lid and shake the jar. Wrap the jar in a cloth and shake it again. What happens?

When the grains hit the sides of the jar, they send vibrations through it, making a rattling sound. The cloth muffles the vibrations, so you don't hear the rattle as clearly.

89 Buzzing hum

Put your lips together and hum as loudly as you can. Fold a sheet of wax paper around a comb. Wrap your lips around it and hum again. Is it louder?

Humming is the sound made when the air in your mouth and nose vibrates. When you hum into the comb, the paper and comb vibrate as well. This magnifies your hum into a louder, buzzy sound.

90 Make a sound tube

Carefully make a small hole with a thumbtack.

Then, push a pencil through to make the hole bigger.

1. Find a wide cardboard tube with a lid, such as a snack tube. Use a thumbtack, then a sharp pencil to poke holes through the tube from one side to the other.

3. Turn the tube upside-down. What do you hear? When the sound stops, turn the tube over and listen again.

2. Slide pencils or pens into the holes, so they stick all the way through the tube. Pour some rice or dried beans into the tube and put on the lid.

As the grains slide along the tube, they bounce off the pencils or pens, making them and the air in the tube vibrate. These bumps and bounces make a pitter-patter noise, a little like raindrops.

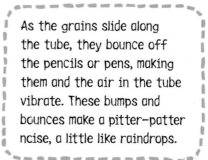

You can vary the sound by putting different things inside the tube, such as dried cous cous or beads.

Make recycled paper

Find out how to make recycled paper, then use the same technique to experiment with different textures and patterns.

91 Rough paper

For a smoother paste, you could mix the paper and water in a blender. (Wash the blender as soon as you have finished using it.)

Use rubber bands to secure the panty hose.

1. Bend a wire coat hanger into a square shape and pull one leg of an old pair of panty hose over it to make a screen.

2. Tear up small pieces of paper into a mixing bowl. Pour in enough water to cover the paper and leave it to soak for an hour.

3. Tear up the soggy paper some more with your fingers. Then, add a tablespoon of white liquid glue and mix it in.

Paper towels will absorb some of the water.

4. Put some paper towels in a baking tray and place your screen on top. Spread the pulpy paper mixture over the screen.

5. Lay a plastic bag on top of the screen and smooth it out with a rolling pin to make a thin layer of pulp under the bag.

It may take 2-3 days to dry completely.

6. Place the screen on some newspaper to dry. The pulp dries to form paper, which you can peel away from the screen.

This paper was made with torn-up pieces of blue and white paper.

Notice how the surface and the edges of the paper look rough and uneven.

Most paper is made from tiny fibers or strands of wood. When old paper is torn up and soaked, these strands separate out. Rolling the pulp squashes the fibers back together to form paper again.

92 Stronger paper

Make some paper using white paper and add small pieces of cotton balls to the mix.

Cotton comes from cotton plants. Cotton fibers are stronger than wood fibers and make paper that tears less easily.

You could add lengths of cotton thread, too.

93 Speckled paper

Add torn-up shiny wrapping paper to your paper pulp.

The shiny paper doesn't break down well, so the shiny shreds show in the recycled paper.

94 Pretty paper

Add a few drops of food dye to the pulp and mix it well. Sprinkle some sequins or glitter over the spread-out pulp, before rolling it flat.

Paper can be dyed many different shades. Adding sequins or glitter creates a sparkly effect.

95 Newspaper

Make a pulp by tearing up old newspapers and magazines.

The ink from the newspapers and magazines makes a darker paper, like this.

96 Petals and leaves

Try making pulp using tissue paper. Add flower petals, leaves or grass to the paper pulp before rolling it.

This paper was made with tissue paper, which gives a smoother pulp.

The petals, grass or leaves will be flattened during the rolling, and be preserved in the paper.

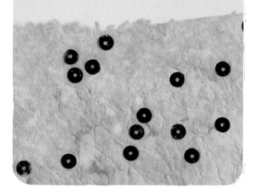

Resisting motion

Discover how things that aren't moving resist starting to move. This is known as inertia.

97 Orange tumble

1. Place a square of cardboard over the top of a plastic pitcher.

2. Stand a cardboard tube on the square and balance an orange on top.

3. Using the palm of your hand, quickly hit the square from the side.

When you hit the square, it flies out sideways and makes the tube fall out to the side, too. But the orange drops straight down into the pitcher. This is because the orange is heavier and heavy objects have more resistance to being moved.

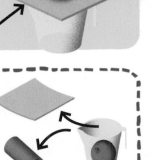

The orange should land in the pitcher.

98 Tablecloth tug

1. Lay a smooth cloth or piece of fabric on a table. Place some heavy plastic cups and plates on top.

2. Give the edge of the cloth a quick, sharp tug to pull it away from the table.

Tug sharply.

You may need to practice this a few times to get it to work.

You should find that the plates and cups want to stay where they are, even when you tug the cloth. This happens because of their inertia – they are heavy enough to resist being moved.

99 Heavy loads

1. Try pushing a skateboard along.

2. Now, put a couple of heavy books on top. How easy is it to push along now?

3. Add more books and see how hard you have to push to move the board.

You need to push the skateboard much harder when it is loaded with books. This is because the heavier something is, the greater its inertia, and the more it resists being moved.

You can see the same effect with a shopping cart. The more groceries you add to the cart, the harder you have to push it to start it moving.

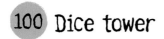

100 Dice tower

1. Stack three dice in a tower. Place a coin on top and then pile three more dice on top of it.

2. Use your middle finger to flick the coin from the middle of the tower. What happens to the dice?

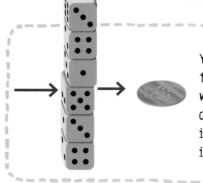

You should be able to flick the coin out without knocking down the dice. This is because of the inertia of the dice.

101 Coin tower

1. Stack ten coins in a tower.

2. Use your middle finger to flick another coin strongly at the bottom of the tower.

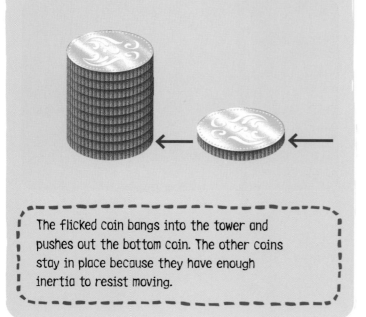

The flicked coin bangs into the tower and pushes out the bottom coin. The other coins stay in place because they have enough inertia to resist moving.

102 Glue-stick topple

1. Place a narrow strip of paper over the edge of a table. Stand a glue stick up on the strip.

2. Slowly try to pull the paper out from under the glue stick. What happens?

Make sure about half of the strip hangs over the edge of the table.

3. Try to remove the paper again, but this time chop at the hanging paper with your hand.

You should find that the glue stick wants to stay where it is. It can't resist the movement of the paper being pulled away slowly, so it topples over. But if you whip the paper away quickly enough, the glue stick can resist and stays standing.

103 Coin catch

1. Hold your hand palm-side up next to your ear and balance a coin on your elbow.

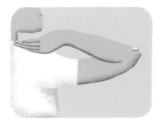

2. Bring your hand forward in one quick movement and try to catch the coin before it falls to the ground.

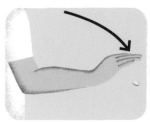

The coin has inertia and it takes a moment before the downward pull of gravity makes it move too quickly to catch. This gives you time to grab it before it's out of reach.

39

Air pressure

Find out about the strength of the air and how this changes at different temperatures.

104 Defy gravity

1. Fill a glass with water, all the way to the top.

Fill it all the way to the brim.

2. Place a piece of card stock on top of the glass and press it down firmly.

3. Hold the card stock firmly in place, and turn over the glass. Slowly let go of the card stock.

Do this part over a sink, just in case.

You should find that the card stock remains in place and the water stays in the glass.

This is because of air pressure pushing up from below. The air pressure is great enough to balance the weight of the water inside the glass.

Water pushing down

Air pressure pushing up

What is air pressure?

Air is made up of tiny particles, which bounce around and push against things – creating air pressure. The air is constantly pushing on us, too, but we're so used to it that we don't notice it's there.

105 Does air have weight?

1. Blow up two balloons to the same size. Tie one balloon to each side of a ruler using string.

2. Tie another piece of string to the middle of the ruler and hang it up.

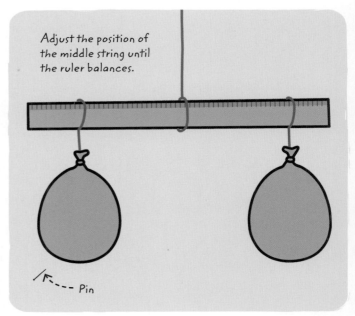

Adjust the position of the middle string until the ruler balances.

Pin

3. Burst one of the balloons with a pin. What happens?

The ruler tips up at the end with the burst balloon, showing that the inflated balloon is heavier than the burst balloon. This is because air *does* have weight.

40

106 Make your own weather forecaster

1. Cut the end off a balloon and stretch it over a jar. Hold it in place with a rubber band.

2. Tape a straw on the balloon, like this.

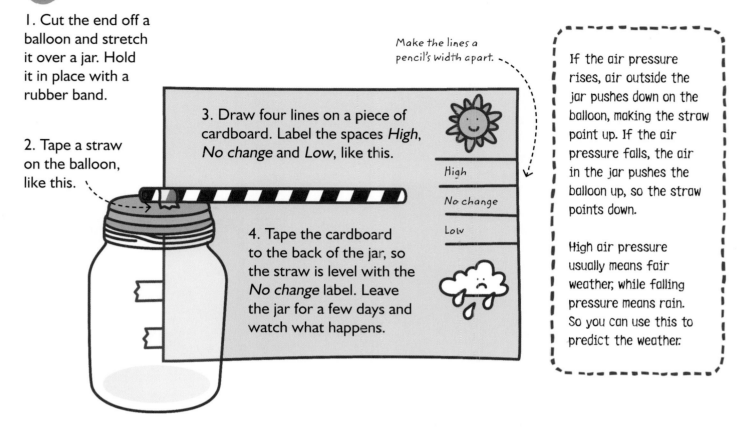

Make the lines a pencil's width apart.

3. Draw four lines on a piece of cardboard. Label the spaces *High*, *No change* and *Low*, like this.

High

No change

Low

4. Tape the cardboard to the back of the jar, so the straw is level with the *No change* label. Leave the jar for a few days and watch what happens.

If the air pressure rises, air outside the jar pushes down on the balloon, making the straw point up. If the air pressure falls, the air in the jar pushes the balloon up, so the straw points down.

High air pressure usually means fair weather, while falling pressure means rain. So you can use this to predict the weather.

107 Balloon in a bottle

1. Fill a bowl with cold water and add some ice. Half-fill a plastic bottle with hot water. Count to ten, then stretch a balloon over the top.

2. Place the bottle in the icy water. Wait for a few minutes and see what happens.

This works best with recently boiled water.

As the bottle cools, the air pressure inside it drops and the balloon is sucked in. The air outside the bottle is at a higher pressure and pushes into the bottle, making the balloon start to inflate inside it.

108 Collapsing bottle

1. Carefully pour some recently boiled water into a plastic bottle and swirl it around.

Put the bottle down in the sink and don't hold it while you pour.

2. After five minutes, empty the bottle and put the lid on. Place the bottle in a freezer or refrigerator for a few minutes, then take it out. What happens?

Wear oven gloves while emptying the bottle.

The bottle comes out squashed. As the air inside the bottle cools, the pressure drops, too. Higher air pressure outside the bottle presses in and crushes it.

Surface tension

Find out more about surface tension on water and use it to create some colorful patterns.

109 Chalky pattern

1. Use a cheese grater carefully to grate some different colors of chalk into a wide dish of water.

Don't grate your fingers.

2. Stir the chalk around with a toothpick to mix the colors a little.

3. Lay some paper on the water for a few seconds, then lift it off. Leave it to dry.

The surface of the water holds together like a skin because of surface tension (see page 22). Chalk dust is light enough to sit on top of this skin, but when you lay paper on top, the chalk sticks to that instead and the pattern transfers to the paper.

Chalk dust on paper

110 Chalky oil

1. Carefully grate some chalk onto a plate. Add a teaspoon of vegetable oil to the dust and mix them well.

Cheese grater

Don't grate your fingers.

2. Using a teaspoon, drip the chalky oil onto a wide dish of water.

3. Swirl the chalky oil gently with a toothpick.

4. Lay some paper on the water, then lift it off and leave it to dry.

The chalky oil spreads out on the surface of the water – and stays on the surface, even if you swirl it. But when you lay the paper on top, the chalky oil sticks to that instead, transferring the pattern.

Chalky oil on paper

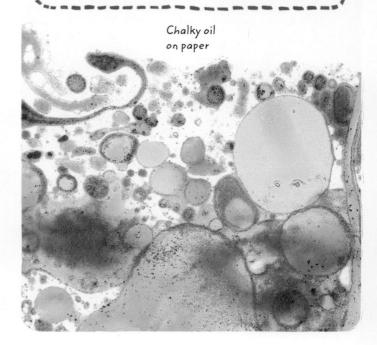

111 Nail polish test

1. Pour some water into a small bowl. Add some drops of nail polish in different colors, like this.

2. Gently drag a toothpick through the nail polish to make a heart shape. Lay some paper over the top, then lift it off.

Swirls of nail polish on water

Nail polish is light enough to sit on the water's surface, and it remains there as you swirl it around. When you lay paper over the pattern, the polish pattern sticks to the paper instead.

112 Oil drops in chalk

Using a cheese grater, carefully grate some chalk over a wide dish of water to make a thin layer of chalk dust. Add some drops of vegetable oil over the chalk and wait for a minute. Lay a sheet of paper on the surface, then lift it off and leave it to dry.

The oil drops spread out on the water's surface, pushing away the chalk dust in circles. You can see the oily circles when you transfer the pattern to paper.

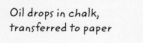

Oil drops in chalk, transferred to paper

113 Shaving foam printing

Cover a wide dish with a layer of shaving foam, then use a paintbrush to spatter the foam with paint. (You can use any kind of paint.) Swirl the paint with a toothpick, then lay a piece of paper on top. Lift off the paper and scrape off the foam with a piece of cardboard to reveal the pattern.

The foam behaves like the skin on the water's surface. The paint sits on the surface of the foam and can be swirled around to make a pattern that transfers to paper.

Shaving foam print

Living things and cells

Cells are tiny building blocks that all living things are made up of. Every cell has a code deep inside it, called DNA, that tells it what to do. You can look at cells and DNA with these activities.

114 See inside a cell

1. Fill a glass with clear vinegar and drop an egg into it. Leave it for a few minutes. What happens?

As the eggshell and vinegar react, you may see bubbles of gas.

2. Leave it for three days. How does it look now? Gently scrape away any traces of broken-down eggshell.

Hold up the shell-less egg to the light.

This is what a shell-less egg looks like when you shine a light through it.

The DNA is stored here.

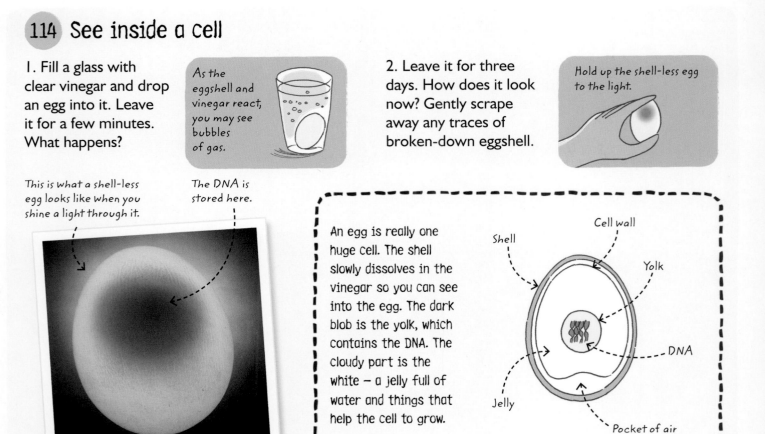

An egg is really one huge cell. The shell slowly dissolves in the vinegar so you can see into the egg. The dark blob is the yolk, which contains the DNA. The cloudy part is the white – a jelly full of water and things that help the cell to grow.

Shell

Cell wall

Yolk

DNA

Jelly

Pocket of air

115 Cells and water

1. Half-fill two glasses with warm water. Stir three tablespoons of salt into one of them.

2. Carefully cut the ends off two carrots. Stand one in each glass. Leave them overnight. What happens?

You should find that the carrot in salt water shrinks and the carrot in plain water swells. Cells contain lots of water, and they react according to how much water and salt there is around them.

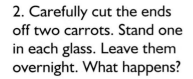

Carrot cells in salty water release water, making the carrot shrink.

Carrot cells in plain water absorb water, making the carrot bigger.

What does DNA look like?

DNA is made up of long, thin strands. The strands are too small to see on their own, but you can see them when they clump together. The clumps look similar, whether they come from plants or animals. But inside, the strands carry very different codes. These codes are what makes a strawberry become a strawberry, for example, and what makes you *you*.

116 See some fruit DNA

1. Place a plastic bottle of rubbing alcohol in the freezer for an hour. (Rubbing alcohol can be bought from a pharmacy.)

2. Put some strawberries and a little water into a plastic sandwich bag. Close it and squash the berries.

3. Open the bag and pour the juice into a glass. Stir in a tiny squirt of dishwashing liquid.

4. Tilt the glass slightly and slowly pour in icy-cold rubbing alcohol until the glass is half full. What do you see? Leave it for an hour. What do you see now?

Do not drink this mixture.

Strands of strawberry DNA clumped together

You can see the strands more clearly if you shine a light through the glass.

Do the activities on this page with an adult. Make sure no one drinks the rubbing alcohol, as it will harm them.

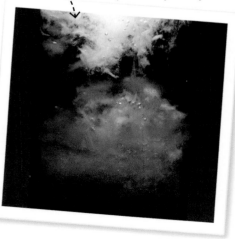

117 See human DNA

1. Place a plastic bottle of rubbing alcohol in the freezer for an hour.

2. Stir a tablespoon of salt into half a glass of water.

3. Take a teaspoon of the salty water, put it in your mouth, swirl it around and spit it out into a new glass.

4. Take another half glass of water and stir in a few drops of dishwashing liquid. Stir a teaspoon of this mixture into the salty spit glass.

5. Tilt the salty spit glass. Slowly pour in cold rubbing alcohol until the glass is half full. Leave it to stand for an hour. Can you see your own DNA?

Do not drink this mixture.

Squashing berries, or swirling salt water in your mouth, lets you collect cells. The dishwashing liquid breaks down the cells and releases their DNA. The rubbing alcohol separates the DNA, which then clumps together to form sticky, cloudy strings.

Building shapes

Learn how some shapes are stronger than others, and are harder to knock down.

Build a tall tower

1. Use short drinking straws and marshmallows to build two squares.

2. Use four more short straws to join the squares, making a cube.

3. Trim six longer straws and add one straw to each square to make a diagonal.

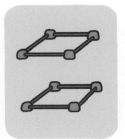 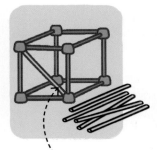 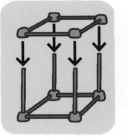

Adding diagonals makes the cube less wobbly.

4. Make more squares. Join them onto the cube to make a tower, adding diagonals as you go. Place a cardboard platform on top and see if the tower can support a toy.

The tower is strong because each side is supported by the sides around it, and the diagonals stop the sides from twisting out of shape. The tower can support a toy because the toy's weight spreads through all the straws and is supported equally by each one.

119 Build a pyramid

1. Build a square using short straws and four marshmallows.

2. Add four longer straws and one marshmallow to make a pyramid.

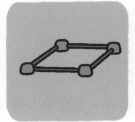 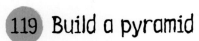

A pyramid is strong because it is good at spreading out weight. If you push on the tip, or lean a book against the side, the weight will spread through the straws and be supported.

3. Test the strength of the pyramid by pushing on its tip. Can you lean a book against the pyramid?

Towering tubes

1. Roll a piece of thick card stock into a round tube. Tape down the edge and stand it upright.

2. Fold a second piece of card stock into a triangular tube. Tape the edge and stand it upright, too.

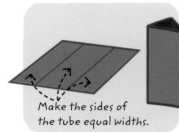

Make the sides of the tube equal widths.

3. Place a square of cardboard over each tube and balance a small toy on top. Now, try balancing something heavier on top. How much weight can each tower support?

Round and triangular tubes are both good at supporting weight. Both shapes share the weight loaded on them as evenly as possible. Triangular tubes with equal sides share the load equally between them. A round tube shares its load along the whole length.

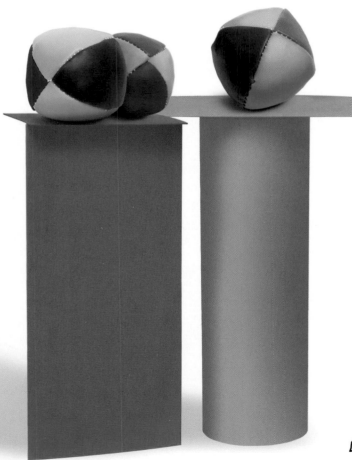

121 Paper tube

1. Roll a piece of paper into a tube. Tape the edge and stand it up. Place an apple on top and let go. Does it stay there?

2. Lay the tube down on its side. Place the apple on the middle and let go. What happens now?

The paper tube is only strong when upright. When it is lying down, its curved shape can't spread out the weight of the apple very well and the tube gets squashed.

122 Balancing bottle

Half-fill a plastic bottle with water. Give it a push near the bottom. Does it topple? Try again nearer the top.

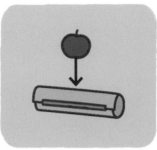

123 Full bottle

Add more water so the bottle is full. Now give it a push near the top. Can you push the bottle over?

How easily the bottle topples depends on where its weight is centered. The bottle is more stable when most of the weight is in the bottom. Filling it up makes the center of the weight higher, which makes the bottle less stable and easier to tip over.

Solids, liquids and goo

In these experiments you can find out more about solids and liquids, and make a strange substance called goo, which is somewhere in-between.

124 Testing solids

1. Gather some solid objects, such as a rubber ball, a towel and an old newspaper.

2. Put the objects in containers of different sizes and take them out again. What happens?

3. Next, try squashing each object. Now try pulling them. Can you tear or twist them?

Test your solid objects:
Can you squeeze...

...tear...

...or twist them?

Everything is made up of millions of tiny particles that are too small to see. Solids don't flow or spread out easily because their particles are very close together, which gives them their shape and makes them firm. Solids keep their shape until something pulls, pushes, stretches or squeezes them. Even then, they often return to their original size and shape.

125 Liquid shapes

Fill a measuring cup with water. Now pour the water into some different shaped containers and then back into the cup. What do you notice?

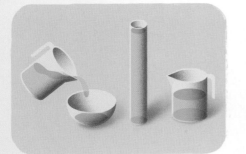

The tiny particles inside liquids are more spaced out than the particles in solids, so they can move. This allows liquids to flow and change shape. When you pour water, it takes the shape of whatever you pour it into.

126 Sugar and water

Stir a spoonful of sugar into a glass of water. What happens? Then, taste the water. What do you notice?

The sugar grains seem to disappear, but the water becomes sweet. In fact, the tiny particles in each sugar grain have spread out and mixed evenly with the particles of water. This is called dissolving.

127 Sand and water

Stir a spoonful of sand into a glass of water. What happens? Leave it for a few minutes. What do you notice? (Don't drink this mixture.)

The sand grains don't seem to disappear because its tiny particles don't dissolve. Instead, sand makes a cloudy mixture called a suspension. After a few minutes, the sand will separate out again and sink to the bottom of the glass.

128 Make some goo

1. Pour two cups of cornstarch into a big bowl. Add four drops of food dye to a cup of water and pour it into the bowl.

2. Mix the ingredients together with your hands until they are well blended.

3. How does the mixture you have made feel in your hands?

4. Scoop up a handful of mixture. Does it stay in your hand or dribble through your fingers?

5. See if you can make a ball by rolling the mixture between your hands. Try rolling it quickly, then slowly.

6. Try punching the mixture with your hand. Does it feel hard or soft?

7. Try to stir the mixture quickly with a wooden spoon. What happens?

Goo can act like both a solid *and* a liquid. Cornstarch is made of lots of long, stringy particles. When the goo is rolled quickly or punched, the particles push back so the goo feels solid. If the goo is dribbled, the particles slide over each other so it feels like a liquid.

129 Make slime

Take the goo from activity 128 (or make some more) and add another cup of water to make slime. Try stirring and rolling it. What happens?

When more water is added, goo turns into a slimy liquid and loses its special nature. You can stir it, but you can't roll it into a ball.

130 Dry slime

1. Pour a thin layer of slime onto a plate. Gently press some objects into it, such as a coin, a paper clip and a leaf.

2. Leave the slime to dry overnight. Then, lift out the objects. What is left behind?

The water in the slime slowly evaporates – it turns into a gas and floats away in the air. Only the dry cornstarch and food dye are left behind. If you leave objects in slime while it dries, you will get imprints of their shapes.

Friction tricks

Find out more about friction (the force you get when things rub together) and how to increase and reduce it.

131 Make a rocket

1. Draw a rocket on a piece of thin cardboard and cut it out.

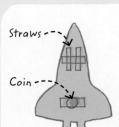

2. Cut two small pieces off a drinking straw and tape them to the rocket. Tape a coin near the bottom of the rocket to add a little weight so it hangs better.

Straws
Coin

3. Cut a piece of string twice as long as your arm. Thread it up through one straw and down through the other, to make a loop.

4. Hang the loop over a coat hook or door handle. Hold the ends of the string apart and pull on each one. Can you make the rocket climb the string?

You could add beads to the ends of the string, like this, to make it easier to grip them.

132 Let it go

Repeat activity 131, but then let go of the string. What happens?

> When you release the tension on the string, there is no friction, so the rocket falls.

You can make the rocket 'hover' by holding the ends of the string apart.

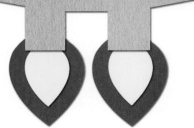

> Friction is the force you get when two things rub together (see pages 14–15). When you pull on the strings, the rocket moves up. Without friction, it would then slide down again (due to the force of gravity, which pulls things downward). But the rubbing of the string against the straw generates enough friction to keep the rocket from falling down.

134 Reducing friction

1. Place a heavy book on a table. Try pushing the book along the table with your little finger. How easy do you find it?

2. Now place several marbles beneath the book and push the book with your little finger again. How does it compare?

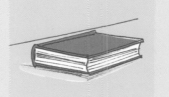

In step 1, there is a lot of friction between the book and the table, so it's hard to move the book. In step 2, the marbles lower the friction by reducing the amount of contact between the book and the table. This makes the book easier to move.

135 Rubbing hands

Rub your hands together quickly for 20 seconds. What happens to them?

Rubbing your hands together creates friction. Friction also makes heat, so your hands start to feel warm.

136 Skiddy feet

Try skidding over a smooth floor in bare feet and notice how it feels. Next, try skidding carefully in your socks, then in sports shoes. How does each compare?

Socks reduce friction between your feet and the floor, so you slide more easily. Sports shoes are designed to have lots of grip and create friction, so it's harder to skid.

133 Rougher string

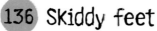

Make another rocket using rougher string or yarn. How does it compare?

Rougher string creates more friction, so it is better at stopping the rocket from sliding down the string.

51

Making music

Find out how making vibrations in the air produces musical sounds.

137 Make some bottle pipes

1. Arrange some different shaped glass bottles in a row.

2. Pour water into them, filling them with different amounts. Blow over the mouth of each bottle. What do you notice?

Blowing over the bottles makes the air in them vibrate, creating sounds. The type of sound you make depends on how much air there is. A little air (in the bottles with more water) makes a higher sound. A lot of air (in the bottles with less water) makes a lower sound.

138 Hit it!

Tapping the bottles makes the air vibrate, too. The less air there is, the higher the sound you make.

Use a spoon or stick to hit gently against the sides of the bottles. What happens?

139 Didgeridoo

1. Fold a piece of wax paper around a plastic comb.

2. Hold this on top of an empty giftwrap tube.

3. Rest the bottom of the tube on a table, lift the top to your mouth, then blow strongly onto the comb. What happens?

This is a simple version of an Australian instrument called a didgeridoo. Blowing the comb through the paper makes buzzing noises. These echo in the tube, making the air vibrate to create loud, rumbling sounds.

140 Speakers

1. Snap your fingers beside your ear and notice how loud the sound is.

2. Next, blow up a balloon. Hold it to your ear and snap your fingers near the opposite side of the balloon. What do you notice now?

When you snap your fingers near the balloon, the air trapped inside it vibrates more than air outside would (as the vibrations bounce around inside the balloon). These strong vibrations magnify the snap, so it sounds louder. The balloon is acting a little like a loud speaker.

Stretch the band around the paper.

Different sizes of drums produce different sounds.

You could combine different sizes of tins to make a drum kit.

141 Loose drum

Loosely place a piece of wax paper over the top of a round tin. Keep it in place with a rubber band. Hit the paper with a spoon. What do you hear?

142 Tight drum

Release the rubber band slightly, pull the paper tight and replace the band. Now hit the paper again. Does it sound different this time?

Hitting the loose paper doesn't make the air inside vibrate very much, so you make a quiet sound. Hitting the tight paper causes lots of vibrations and the sound is much louder.

143 Make some panpipes

1. Take seven wide drinking straws. Leave the first straw full length. Cut about 1in (2cm) off the second, 2in (4cm) off the third, and so on.

Keep the pieces you snip off.

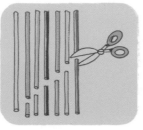

The spacers make it easier to blow into one straw at a time.

2. Arrange the straws in a row from the longest to the shortest, making sure their tops line up. Place a piece of snipped-off straw between each pair as a spacer, like this.

3. Wrap a length of tape around all the straws and spacers to hold them in place.

4. Lift the panpipes to your lips. Blow over the longest straw. How does it sound? Now try the others. What do you notice?

The longer straws have more air inside. When you blow over them, they vibrate and you hear a low sound. The shorter straws have less air and make higher sounds. This is how several musical instruments work, including organs and (real) panpipes.

You and some friends could play all the instruments together to form a band.

Layered liquids

Find out how some liquids separate into layers, and how you can make them mix together.

144 Three-in-one

1. Put four tablespoons of water in a tall glass and add a few drops of food dye.

2. Add four tablespoons of vegetable oil to the glass. Don't stir the oil and water.

3. Then, add four tablespoons of honey. Don't stir it, and watch what happens.

When water, oil and honey are put together, they separate into layers. The layers form according to how dense the liquids are (how heavy and how spread out the particles inside them are – see the "Density" box on page 5). Oil is less dense than water or honey, so it sits on the top. Honey is more dense, so it sinks to the bottom.

145 Stir it up

Repeat activity 144, but stir the oil, water and honey well with a spoon. Leave the mixture for five minutes. What happens?

You could try other liquids to see if they separate into layers, too. This picture shows some other possibilities.

Olive oil

Water and food dye

Honey

Olive oil

Water and food dye

Vegetable oil

Water and food dye

Maple syrup

Vegetable oil

Water and food dye

Liquid soap

Honey

146 Different order

Add water, honey and oil in a different order. Does it make any difference to the end result?

Whichever way you introduce oil, honey and water, or try to mix them, eventually they will always separate into layers, with the oil on top and the honey at the bottom.

147 Oil and vinegar

1. Put three tablespoons of olive oil into a clean jar with a lid and add one tablespoon of wine vinegar.

2. Add a pinch of sugar and some salt and pepper.

3. Close the lid and shake the jar well, then leave it for five minutes. Watch what happens.

At first, the vinegar and oil appear to mix. But after a while, they separate into layers. Vinegar sinks to the bottom because it is denser than oil.

You can use the shaken-up oil and vinegar as salad dressing.

148 Add an egg yolk

1. Break an egg into your hand and let the white slip through your fingers into a bowl. Put the yolk in another bowl and beat it with a fork.

Wash your hands after touching the raw egg.

2. Shake up some olive oil and wine vinegar in a jar, as in activity 147. Add the yolk to the jar, close the lid and shake it well. What happens?

When you add an egg yolk, the oil and vinegar stay mixed. The yolk sticks to the oil and vinegar, stopping them from separating out. This type of mixture is called an emulsion.

The oil, vinegar, egg mixture you make is mayonnaise.

149 Sinking and rising

1. Pour water into a tall glass or bottle until it is two thirds full. Add a few drops of food dye.

2. Add a few tablespoons of vegetable oil. Leave it to settle.

3. Now add a few pinches of salt. What happens?

4. Add more salt to continue seeing the effect.

The salt sinks to the bottom, taking droplets of oil with it. The salt then dissolves in the water and the oil rises to the surface because it is less dense than water. The effect stops when all the salt has dissolved.

Watching wildlife

Scientists called zoologists study animals. Here are some simple things you can do to attract animals, so you too can study how they behave.

150 Make butterfly food

Mix a cup of sugar with four cups of water. Soak some pieces of sponge in the mixture. Then, put them on the branches of a tree, or an outside windowsill, and wait for butterflies to come and feed.

Butterflies use their long tube-like mouthparts to suck up their food.

Butterflies normally feed on a sugary liquid called nectar, found in flowers. Sugar and water is similar to nectar, and butterflies will visit sponges soaked in it.

151 Make bird feeders

You can attract birds by building simple feeders and hanging them up outside. It is especially good to feed birds in winter, when food is short. Here are three ideas to try...

Feeder 1
Tie some string to the bottom of a big pinecone. Smear the cone with peanut butter, roll it in birdseed, then hang it up.

Many garden birds feed on seeds, fruit and nuts. Different kinds of birds prefer different foods, and feed in different ways, so you can watch which birds visit which feeder. Birds often come back again and again once they've found a source of food.

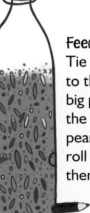

Pencil

Feeder 3
Knot the ends of a long piece of string. Thread some pieces of cereal, toast or dried fruit onto it and hang it up.

Feeder 2
Use a thumbtack carefully to make two holes on opposite sides near the base of a plastic bottle. Twist a blunt pencil through the holes. Then, make two bigger holes above them. Pour birdseed into the bottle and screw on the cap. Tie some string around the neck and hang it up.

152 Make a wormery

1. Find some garden soil containing worms. You might also find worms under rocks or leaves. Fill a flower pot with the soil and the worms.

2. Carefully cut the top and bottom off a large plastic bottle.

3. Stand the middle part of the bottle on top of the pot and fill it with thick layers of soil and thin layers of crushed chalk and small stones.

4. Sprinkle some leaves and grass on top. Use a felt-tip pen to mark the levels of the layers on the side of the bottle.

Make sure there is always a little water in the saucer.

5. Wrap some dark paper around the bottle and add water to the saucer. Leave the wormery for a few days.

6. After several days, remove the paper. What has happened to the layers? Now put the worms back where you found them.

The layers will be mixed up and you may see shreds of grass and leaves deep in the soil. This is because worms eat decaying plant parts and take in a little soil too while they eat. As they find, eat and digest their food, they churn up the soil.

153 Soil bugs

1. Carefully cut off the top third of a plastic bottle and place it upside down inside the lower part. Pack some soil into the top, with the lid off.

2. Look at the soil. Can you see any creatures crawling in it? Shine a flashlight on the top of the soil. What happens? Return the soil and any creatures afterward.

Many bugs, such as worms and beetles, live in soil. They don't like bright light, so they will crawl away from the flashlight and fall through the mouth of the bottle.

154 Undercover bugs

Leave an empty flower pot upside down in a flower bed or on some grass overnight. Lift it up gently the next day. Can you spot anything?

Lots of bugs, such as woodlice, beetles, earwigs and slugs, like to live in dark, damp, sheltered places, so an upside-down pot will attract them.

Magnet experiments

Explore how you can use magnets to build structures and move things.

155 Paper clip dangle

1. Hold up a magnet and wave a metal paper clip near it. Does it stick to the magnet?

2. How many paper clips can you hang in a row?

Magnets pull some metals, such as iron and nickel, toward them. Most metal paper clips contain iron or nickel, so they are pulled toward the magnet. The pull will probably be strong enough to hold several paper clips in a row. When the paper clips get too far from the magnet, the pull becomes too weak, so you can't add any more to the chain.

These are bar magnets, but you can use any kind of magnet, even a refrigerator magnet.

Magnets vary in strength. A strong magnet will hold several paper clips in a row, while a weak magnet might only be able to hold one.

156 Metal tower

Place a magnet on a table. Stack a few metal nuts on top. (You can buy these in a hardware store.) Add some more nuts. How high can you go? Can you push the stack over?

Most nuts contain iron or nickel, so the magnet pulls the first nuts toward it, making the tower strong and stable. The pull gets weaker as the tower gets taller. Eventually, the pull is so weak that the top of the tower will start to wobble.

157 Magnet strength

Put a nut on a table and bring a magnet toward it. How close does it need to be before the nut is pulled toward it?

If you use another magnet, do you see any difference?

A strong magnet can pull the nut from farther away than a weaker one.

158 Underwater trick

Drop a metal paper clip into a glass of water. Can you pull the paper clip out of the water without getting your fingers, or the magnet, wet?

Magnets work through water, so you should be able to get the paper clip by dragging the magnet along the bottom and up the side of the glass.

159 Table trick

1. Put a bolt inside a cardboard box. Move a magnet along the side of the box. What happens?

2. Can you move the box by dragging the magnet along underneath the table?

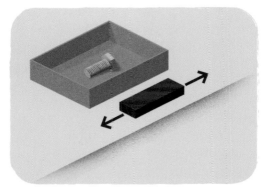

Magnets work even through solid objects, such as the box and the table. This means you can make the bolt move (which moves the box) without touching either of them.

160 Magnet-friendly metals

Try using a magnet to pick up different metal objects, such as some aluminum foil, a copper coin, a brass screw and an iron nail. Here are some other ideas...

Lots of tiny household items are made of metal. These paper clips are made of metal wire covered in plastic.

Not all metals are attracted by magnets. Objects that contain iron or steel are attracted most strongly. Magnets have no effect on aluminum foil.

161 Make a magnet

1. Take a nail that is attracted to magnets and tape it to a piece of paper. Rub a magnet along it about 10 times, in one direction.

2. Remove the tape. Wave the nail slowly over a pile of paper clips. What happens?

Rubbing the nail over and over with a magnet turns the nail itself into a magnet, so it will pull the paper clips toward it — just like the original magnet.

Wind power

See how to make paper pinwheels and use the power of the wind.

162 Make a curved pinwheel

Make the sides about 8in (20cm) long.

1. Draw straight lines from corner to corner on a square of paper. Cut a quarter of the way along each line.

2. To make a sail, bend every other corner into the middle, without creasing the paper. Glue the corners in the middle.

3. Push a thumbtack through the middle of the sail into a cardboard tube and put a ball of poster tack onto its point. Now blow the sail.

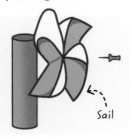

Sail

Your breath pushes against the pinwheel's paper sail to make it turn. Wind is used in a similar way to turn huge wind turbines to produce electricity.

163 Make a square pinwheel

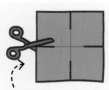

Make the sides about 8in (20cm) long.

1. To make a square sail, draw a cross on a square of card stock. Cut a slit a quarter of the way along each line.

2. Fold every other side up toward the middle. Push a thumbtack through the middle into a cardboard tube and put poster tack on the point. Blow on the sail.

This part of the pinwheel is called its sail.

Thumbtack

Air pushing against the bent paper makes the pinwheel sail turn.

164 More puff

Hold your pinwheel in front of a fan or hair dryer. Does the sail turn more quickly?

A fan or hair dryer blows more strongly than your breath and makes the sail spin faster.

Air pushes against the folded edges to make this pinwheel sail turn.

165 Spinning straw

1. Make a square sail as in activity 163, then make a small hole in the middle with a sharp pencil. Push a straw through the hole, so it fits tightly.

2. Use a thumbtack to make two holes opposite each other at the top of a cardboard tube. Twist a pencil in the holes to make them slightly bigger.

3. Push the straw through both holes. Can you make the straw turn by blowing on the pinwheel sail?

> When the sail turns, the straw turns, too. The straw works like a shaft, or pole, inside a traditional windmill. The shaft was used to turn huge millstones to grind grains of wheat into flour.

166 Lifting things

Take the pinwheel from activity 165 and tie a piece of string to the straw, as shown here. Tie the other end of the string to a small, light object, such as a pencil sharpener. Blow on the sail. What happens?

> As the sail turns, the straw turns and winds up the string, lifting the object. This shows how wind power can be used to lift or move things.

167 Lift a loaded carton

Repeat activity 166, but tie an empty yogurt carton to the end of the string. Put a few rice grains or paper clips into the carton and see how much the pinwheel can lift when you blow.

You may need to tape down the base to stop the pinwheel from tipping over.

Tie the string behind the sail.

As the string winds around the straw, it lifts the pencil sharpener into the air.

61

Separating inks

Most colored inks are actually made up of lots of colors. Activity 168 shows you how to separate them. Then there are several variations to try.

This ink from an orange felt-tip pen is a mixture of pink, orange and yellow.

168 Felt-tip pen ink

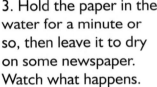

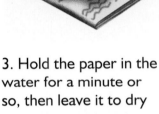

1. Cut up a coffee filter paper to leave a flat piece, like this. Draw a line on it, a little above the bottom, with a felt-tip pen.

2. Dip the bottom of the paper in a saucer of water, making sure the pen line stays above the water.

3. Hold the paper in the water for a minute or so, then leave it to dry on some newspaper. Watch what happens.

Ink is usually made from a mixture of colors. When the water soaks up the paper and touches the ink, the ink dissolves, spreading out and separating into different colors. This is called chromatography.

Red felt-tip pen

Blue felt-tip pen

Brown felt-tip pen

The original felt-tip line is here.

Black felt-tip pen

169 Many colors

Try out different colored markers on other pieces of filter paper and compare the patterns they make.

The colors and patterns made by different inks will vary, depending on what they contain. Some colors dissolve more easily in the water and travel farther as they spread through the paper.

170 High line

Draw a line higher up a piece of filter paper, then dip the bottom end in the water as before. Is the result the same?

This line was drawn higher up the filter paper, but the ink has still dissolved and spread out.

Green felt-tip pen

The water takes longer to reach the ink, but the ink dissolves and separates in a similar way.

171 Ordinary paper

Repeat activity 168 using ordinary writing or printer paper. Does anything happen?

172 Other papers

Repeat activity 168 with other types of paper, such as paper towels or newspaper. Notice how the ink spreads.

The ink spreads less well on printer paper than filter paper because printer paper is less absorbent. The ink spreads more on paper towels because paper towels are more absorbent. The more absorbent the paper, the faster the water spreads and the faster the ink dissolves and separates.

Felt-tip pen on paper towels

173 Ballpoint pen

Draw a line on coffee filter paper with a ballpoint pen. What happens this time?

Ballpoint pens contain waterproof ink. This kind of ink won't separate because it doesn't dissolve in water.

174 Middle spot

Cut out a circle of coffee filter paper. Draw a big spot in the middle with a felt-tip pen. Drip a few drops of water on the ink. What happens?

Brown felt-tip pen

The colors separate and spread out in a circle as the water socks through the paper in every direction.

63

Fruit and fruit juices

Explore some of the properties of various fruits and their juices with these activities.

175 Pulp and juice

1. Place an orange segment in a sieve. Hold it over a bowl and squash it with a fork.

2. Taste the pulp that is left in the sieve, then the juice in the bowl. Which has the strongest taste?

The juice contains most of the taste in a fruit – not the pulp.

176 Hard and soft

1. Try crushing a piece of hard fruit, such as a slice of apple. Do you get any juice?

2. Now crush some soft fruit, such as raspberries. Do they give you more juice?

Some fruits naturally contain more juice than others. The juice is stored in little bags called juice sacs.

In hard fruits, such as apples, the sacs are tiny and difficult to break, so it's hard to get the juice out without cooking the fruits or using a juicer.

In soft fruits, such as raspberries and oranges, the sacs are bigger and easier to break, so the juice comes out quickly.

The juice sacs are large enough to see.

177 Sweet and sour

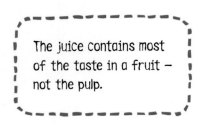

Crush the fruit through a sieve into a bowl.

1. Crush a slice of ripe, fresh peach or nectarine into a bowl. Is it sweet or sour?

2. Squeeze a slice of lemon onto a plate and taste the juice. Compare the two tastes.

Lemons have some sugar in their juice, but they also have a lot of acid, which makes them taste sour.

Fruits such as peaches and nectarines contain a little acid and a lot of sugar, making them taste sweeter.

178 Drying fruit

1. Fill a plastic cup one third full with baking soda, then fill it to the top with salt. Pour the mixture back and forth between two cups to mix it.

2. Cut two thick slices from an apple. Put one in an empty plastic cup, then pour in enough of the mixture to cover it.

3. Put the other apple slice in a clean cup. Leave both cups somewhere away from direct sunlight.

4. A week later, pour the apple slices onto a plate. What has happened to them?

The exposed slice of apple will have shrunk a lot. This is because the moisture in its juice allowed bacteria to grow, making it start to rot away. The mixture on the other slice dried it out, protecting it from bacteria and preserving it.

Dried apple   Exposed apple

⚠ Use the knife carefully, and don't eat the apple slices after this activity: they may make you sick.

179 Juice stains

⚠ Wear old clothes and protect surfaces when you do this experiment, in case you spill any juice.

1. Put a few blackberries in a sieve, then use a fork to squash them into a bowl.

2. Lay some white cotton material on a newspaper. (You could use an old T-shirt, handkerchief or dish towel.)

3. Paint a pattern on the cotton using the blackberry juice. Leave the cotton to dry.

4. Rinse the cotton under the faucet. Can you still see the pattern on the material?

Lots of fruit juices contain tannin, which is a kind of dye. Blackberry juice has so much tannin in it that it stains material and won't rinse out in water.

You could try making patterns with different juices, such as orange, tomato or cranberry.

Wind direction

Here are some different ways to test the direction of the wind.

180 Make a windsock

Make the four pieces of string the same length.

1. Cut a big square of tissue paper and a strip of card stock. Glue the card stock to the top of the paper.

2. Bend the card stock into a circle. Glue the ends of the card stock firmly together.

3. Tape the tissue paper along the seam to make a tube. Glue tissue-paper triangles to the bottom.

4. Tape four strings to the card stock. Tie the loose ends to a stick. Hold the windsock up in the air on a breezy day. What happens?

On a breezy day, the wind fills the windsock with air and makes it fly. The wind direction is the direction the wind blows from, which is opposite to the direction the windsock is pointing. In strong wind, the windsock flies horizontally, and in low wind, it droops.

181 Make a wind arrow

Tape the coin here.

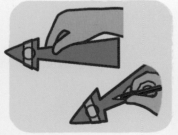

1. Cut out an arrow from card stock, and tape a small coin to its head. Cut a length of strong thread as long as your arm.

2. Hold the arrow in two fingers until it hangs roughly level. Gently push a sharp pencil through this point to make a hole.

3. Push the thread through the hole and knot the ends to make a loop. Hold the arrow in the wind. What happens?

The arrow turns until it points into the wind.
The wind pushes more strongly against the tail of the arrow because it is wider and has a bigger surface area than the head. This pushes the arrow around until the tail is as far as possible from the wind, leaving the arrow head pointing to the wind direction.

182 Finger test

Lick your finger and hold it up in the wind. Does one side feel colder than the other?

Wet skin feels colder where the wind blows on it. The side where your finger feels the coldest shows the direction of the wind.

If this end of the windsock is pointing south, the wind is blowing from the north.

183 Blowing hair

Stand in the wind and turn around until the wind blows your hair away from your face.

When you can feel the wind blowing evenly on your face, sweeping your hair straight back, you are facing the wind direction.

184 Dish towel flag

Take a dish towel or handkerchief and hold it by the corners on one side, so it can catch the wind.

The dish towel flies like a flag in the direction the wind is blowing. This is opposite to the direction that the wind blows from.

185 Make a wind vane

1. Cut a square of card stock. Label the corners N, E, S, W (for north, east, south and west) in a clockwise direction, like this.

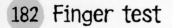

2. Take a sharp pencil with an eraser and push it through the middle of the square, with the letters facing upward.

3. Push the pencil into a plastic cup and attach the cup to an old plate with poster tack. (Make a thumbtack hole first.)

4. Cut out two card stock triangles, one bigger than the other. Tape them to a straw to make an arrow.

5. Push a pin through the straw into the pencil eraser. Place the wind vane outside, so the N on the square points north. (You can use a compass to find which way is north.)

When the wind blows, the arrow turns to point into the wind. You can look at the letters on the card stock to see which direction the wind is blowing from.

Leaves and bark

Find out how leaves take in food and water, and discover more about how plants grow.

186 Make leaf prints

1. Collect some leaves.

2. Lay a leaf on some newspaper. Brush paint over the rougher side of the leaf.

3. Press the painted side of the leaf down on some paper to make a print. Do it twice. Make more prints with other leaves.

4. Compare the patterns of different leaves. What are the similarities? Can you see lots of lines in each leaf?

The lines in the prints are made by veins in the leaves. Veins are thin tubes that carry water and food around the plant.

187 Compare leaf shapes

Arrange some different types of leaves on a piece of paper. Draw around each one with a pencil and compare the shapes. You could color the shapes to record how the leaves look.

Fan-shaped leaves have gaps between each section.

Some leaves have several small leaflets growing from the stalk.

Others have a simple shape with one leaf on each stalk.

Some leaves are prickly.

Some have frilly edges.

Some have wavy edges.

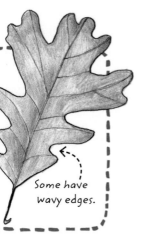

Leaves come in different shapes and sizes to help plants survive in different conditions. Plants make food in their leaves using sunlight. Some leaves have gaps to allow more light to reach lower down the plant. Others are prickly to stop animals from eating them.

188 Dried leaves

1. Place some leaves between two sheets of paper inside a book.

2. Close the book and stack some heavy books on top. Leave them for two weeks. Then, take out the pressed leaves.

3. Compare the pressed leaves with some fresh leaves. How do they differ?

Pressing leaves flattens and dries them, which helps to preserve them. Removing moisture stops the leaves from rotting. It also makes them more brittle. The color of the leaves may fade as some of the parts inside start to break down.

189 Make bark rubbings

Hold some paper against the bark of a tree. Using the side of a wax crayon, rub over the paper until the bark pattern shows. Do more rubbings on different trees and see what kinds of patterns you get.

Bark is a tough, protective layer on the outside of a tree. Some trees, such as oaks, have thick, bumpy bark that stops them from drying out and insulates them against hot and cold weather. Other trees, such as birches, have smooth bark that peels off easily. This helps in damp areas, where harmful mold might grow on soggy bark.

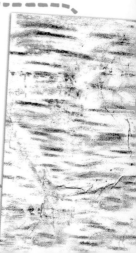

Loud sounds

Learn about how even tiny vibrations cause sounds, explore how sound travels and find out how to make sounds louder.

190 Whisper tube

1. Ask a friend to stand an arm's length away from you and to whisper something. Can you hear what is said?

2. Now hold one end of a long cardboard tube to your ear and try again. Can you hear anything this time?

The whisper is quiet, but the tube magnifies the vibrations. This means it makes them bigger, so it is much easier to hear them.

191 Pop experiment

Hook your middle finger inside your mouth. Close your lips and pop your finger out by pushing it against the inside of your cheek. Try again, but this time puff up your cheeks.

When you pop your finger, the air in your mouth vibrates and you hear a pop. If you puff up your cheeks, there is more air vibrating and the pop sounds stronger.

Vibrations and sounds

Sounds are created by things moving or vibrating (see page 34). Small vibrations make quiet sounds and large vibrations make louder ones.

192 Tap test

Stand beside a table, tap the surface with your finger and listen to the sound it makes. Now, rest your ear on the table and tap again. Can you hear a difference?

The tap should sound louder when your ear is resting on the table. This is because sound vibrations travel even better through solid things than through the air.

193 Make a string telephone

1. Use a sharp pencil to make a small hole in the base of two plastic cups.

2. Cut a very long piece of string. Thread one end through the hole in one of the cups and make a big knot inside.

3. Fix the other end of the string in the other cup in the same way. Ask someone to take that cup into another room and hold it to one ear. Speak into your cup. Can the other person hear you?

Keep the string stretched tight and don't let it touch anything.

Speaking into the cup makes the air inside it vibrate. The cup picks up the vibrations, which travel along the string. The other cup passes the vibrations back into the air, so they can be heard again as sounds.

194 Make a megaphone

1. Cut a large square of drawing paper (or three layers of newspaper).

2. Roll the paper into a cone, then tape the edges together.

3. Snip off the small end to make a mouthpiece. Trim the large end, too, to make it even.

4. Now, speak or sing into the small end. What happens?

5. Place some earphones near the small end of the cone. Try playing something softly through them. Does it sound louder through the cone?

Your voice (or music) echoes around the cone and makes the air inside it vibrate a lot. This magnifies the sound, making it louder.

195 Radio sounds

1. Loosely place a circle of wax paper over the top of a round tin without a lid, and stretch a large rubber band around it.

2. Scatter a few dried beans or grains of rice on the paper. Place the tin by some speakers and turn on some music. What happens?

The sound from the speakers makes the surrounding air vibrate. This makes the paper on the tin vibrate too, bouncing the beans around on the top.

196 Glass speaker

1. Turn on a television or radio. Turn the volume up a little, then go into the next room. Can you hear it?

2. Now, hold a glass against the wall between the rooms and place your ear next to it. What can you hear now?

Vibrations are stronger in solid things than in air, so sound travels more clearly to your ear through the wall and the glass than through the air alone. The vibrations bounce around inside the glass, making the sound louder, too.

Light and rainbows

Find out how to make rainbows by splitting light into different colors.

It's best to use a tall glass so the light passes through more water and makes a clearer rainbow.

197 Make a rainbow in a glass

1. This activity works best on a really sunny day. Fill a glass with water.

A vase or jar would work, too.

2. Hold the glass up to the sunlight and over a piece of white paper.

3. Twist the glass until you see a faint band of colors on the paper – your very own rainbow.

Light is made up of different colors. When it shines through water, it is split up into the colors of a rainbow: red, orange, yellow, green, blue, indigo and violet. This is what happens when the sun shines through raindrops, making a rainbow in the sky.

198 Paint a rainbow

1. Place a glass of water in bright sunshine next to a piece of paper. Turn the glass until a rainbow shines clearly on the paper.

2. Brush colored paints over where the light shines to make a picture of the real rainbow.

199 Make a rainbow in the dark

Shine a flashlight through a glass of water in a darkened room and twist the glass a little until a rainbow appears on the wall.

200 Sky in a jar

Add half a teaspoon of milk to a jar full of water. Shine a flashlight into it. You should see a sky-blue glow.

The milky water splits the light into different colors. Some of the colors go straight through the mix, but the blue bounces off the tiny particles of milk, creating a blue glow. This effect, known as scattering, is also what makes the sky appear blue.

201 Rainbow bath

1. Prop a mirror at one end of a dish full of water. Shine a flashlight at the part of the mirror under the water.

2. Hold a piece of white paper behind the flashlight. Can you see a rainbow shining on it?

As the light shines through the water, it is split up into rainbow colors. The mirror reflects the rainbow back so you can see it on the paper.

202 Outdoor rainbow

On a really sunny day, you can make an outdoor rainbow. Fill a spray bottle with water and spray a fine mist into the sunshine. Look at the mist – do you see a rainbow? (Make sure you do not look directly at the sun.)

You can see the same effect in the spray from garden sprinklers on a bright, sunny day.

203 Rainbow paper

Fill a bowl with water. Add a few drops of clear nail polish and spread them out with a toothpick. Dip some black paper into the bowl, then take it out and leave it to dry. Tilt the paper in the sunlight. What do you see?

The polish forms thin, shiny layers on the paper. When light bounces off these layers, it is split up into different colors, making rainbow patterns.

Fingerprints

Find out how to collect fingerprints and use them to identify people.

204 Make a powder print

1. Press a thumb or finger onto a glass. Then, sprinkle some talcum powder on a plate.

It helps if your fingers are sticky or greasy.

2. Dip a brush into the powder and dust it on the glass. Brush away any extra powder.

3. Place the sticky part of some tape over the fingerprint, then peel away the tape.

4. Press the tape onto a piece of dark paper, then remove it. What do you see?

You should see a white fingerprint on the paper. The skin on your fingers is made up of a pattern of ridges, covered by sweat and oils from your body. These ridges leave an oily mark on the glass, which the powder sticks to. The print is then transferred to the paper by the tape.

You could do this activity again using other types of fine powder, such as chalk dust or flour. You could also try cocoa powder on white paper.

205 Looking for clues

Look for fingerprints on objects around your home. If you can't spot them easily, brush a little talcum powder or chalk dust onto the surface. Do some surfaces reveal fingerprints more easily than others?

DVDs

Mirror

Computer screen

Mouse

Door handle

Lamp

Keyboard

Vase

Plate

Phone

Mug

People leave oily fingerprints on all kinds of surfaces without realizing it. Fingerprints show more clearly on smooth, hard surfaces such as glass, plastic and metal.

206 Paint prints

1. Make an inkpad by pouring a little paint onto an old sponge.

2. Gently press one of your fingers into the paint on the sponge.

3. Press your finger onto some white paper. Repeat this a few times.

The pattern of lines and ridges on your finger should show clearly in the paint print. A similar method is used to take fingerprints at airports and for personal identity cards.

207 Different patterns

Take thumb or fingerprints from different people. Compare the prints. Do any have similar patterns? Are any exactly the same?

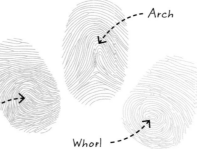

Arch

Loop

Whorl

Some fingerprints have similar shapes. There are three main types: loop, arch, and whorl. But everyone has a unique fingerprint pattern, which means that no two people have fingerprints that are exactly the same. Even the fingerprints of twins are not identical.

208 Fingerprint match

Label the fingerprints from activity 207 with each person's name. Now leave the room, while one person makes a new fingerprint. Can you work out who made the new print?

You should be able to identify who made the print by looking closely at the fingerprint pattern. It may help to use a magnifying glass.

209 Handprints

Brush paint over the palm of your hand, then press it firmly on some white paper. Take some handprints from other people, too. Then compare the patterns.

There are strong lines on your palm that show in a print. Every person has a unique pattern of lines on their palm, which means that no two people have the same handprint patterns. Handprints are sometimes used by the police to identify and catch criminals.

You should see two or three longer lines here.

This big area is the palm.

Staining and bleaching

Many plants contain natural ingredients that will stain or bleach things. Find out how you can use them to make your own paints.

⚠️ Ask an adult to help with the hot water and chopping. It's a good idea to wear an apron, and cover the table with old newspapers.

210 Tea brown

Take the teabags out of the mug.

1. Put five tea bags into a mug. Half-fill the mug with hot water from a kettle, stir the mixture and let it cool.

2. Dip a brush into the tea mixture. Paint a turtle shape and leave it to dry.

Tea and coffee stain the paper brown. Tea leaves contain ingredients called tannins, which make a brown dye. Coffee makes an even darker brown, which is why it shows up over the tea.

211 Coffee brown

1. Spoon three heaped teaspoons of instant coffee into a mug and add a tablespoon of hot water from a kettle.

2. Stir the coffee mixture well and use it to add a face and dark patches to your turtle.

212 Lemon bleach

Use a clean brush to dab dots of lemon juice in the middle of the dark patches. What happens?

Lemon juice acts as a natural bleach: it removes the color, making a pale patch in the middle of the brown.

This picture was painted using natural liquids that dye and bleach things.

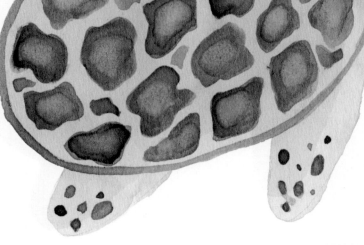

213 Curry yellow

Put two heaped teaspoons of turmeric or curry powder in a mug with two tablespoons of water. Mix it well, then paint a sea floor.

214 Onion orange

1. Carefully peel three brown onions and put the skins in a pan.

2. Add 2in (5cm) of water. Heat the water until it boils. Then, let it simmer for 15 minutes.

3. Leave the mixture to cool, then strain the liquid into a jar. Use it to paint some fish.

215 Beet red

1. Put some roughly chopped beets in a pan, add 2in (5cm) of water and boil them. Let them simmer for 15 minutes, then leave them to cool.

2. Remove the beets and pour the liquid into a jar. (You can eat the beets in a salad.)

3. Use the liquid to add faces and stripes to your fish. Then, mix a little liquid with some water and paint some pink fish.

You could use the juice from a package of pre-boiled beets.

216 Leaf green

Place some chopped grass and spinach leaves in a pan. Add 2in (5cm) of water, bring it to a boil, then let it simmer for 30 minutes. Leave it to cool, then strain the liquid into a jar. Use it to paint some reeds.

Turmeric, used in curry powder, makes a yellow dye. Brown onion skins produce an orange dye. Beets make a pinkish-red dye. The dye made by grass and spinach leaves is yellowish green.

Making rain

Try these experiments to discover how water forms clouds and rain.

217 Make a cloud in a bottle

1. Fill a clear plastic bottle one third full with warm water. Put the lid on. Shake the bottle hard a few times.

2. Remove the lid. Ask an adult to light a match and drop it into the bottle. Put the lid back on.

3. Squeeze and shake the bottle for 20 seconds. Then, slowly release it. What happens? Squeeze and release it again. What do you see?

Shaking helps the water to turn into vapor.

When you squeeze and shake the bottle, water vapor forms inside it. When you let go of the bottle, this vapor turns into a cloud made of water droplets. The particles in the smoke from the match help the droplets to form. When you squeeze the bottle again, the cloud turns back into vapor and disappears.

Squeezing the bottle increases the pressure and temperature, turning droplets into vapor. Releasing the bottle turns the vapor back into water droplets.

The Rain Cycle

This is how real clouds and rain are formed.

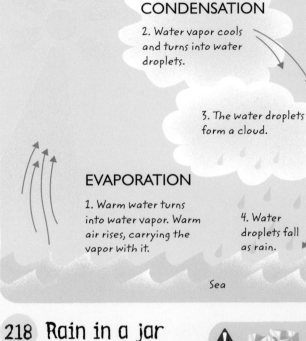

CONDENSATION

2. Water vapor cools and turns into water droplets.

3. The water droplets form a cloud.

EVAPORATION

1. Warm water turns into water vapor. Warm air rises, carrying the vapor with it.

4. Water droplets fall as rain.

Sea

218 Rain in a jar

Pour some recently boiled water into a glass jar and cover it with a piece of foil. After a minute, put some ice cubes on the foil. See what happens.

The hot water turns into vapor and rises inside the jar. The cold foil makes the vapor cool and turn back into water droplets, which fall like rain.

219 Condensation

Pour some recently boiled water into a glass, place a plastic cup on top and wait for a minute. Take the plastic cup off and look inside. What do you see?

Hot water turns into vapor at the surface and rises. As it rises, it cools and forms water droplets inside the top cup. This is known as condensation.

220 Making dew

Half-fill a glass with ice. Add enough cold water to cover the ice. Watch the outside of the glass. What do you see?

You should see water droplets form on the outside of the glass. Air always contains some water vapor. When the glass gets cold, it turns the water vapor from the air into water droplets. Dew forms in a similar way.

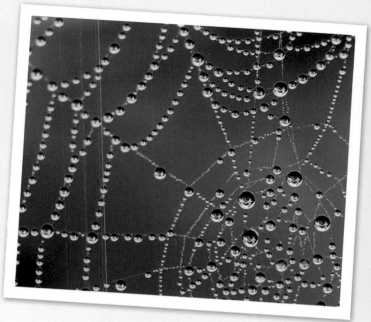

221 Steaming up

Put a small mirror in the refrigerator for 15 minutes. Take it out and blow on it. What happens?

There is water vapor in your breath. When this vapor touches the cold mirror, it forms water droplets on the surface.

Look for drops of dew on grass, flowers or cobwebs in the early morning. Dew forms when water vapor in the air touches cold things and turns into droplets.

222 Make a rain gauge

1. Take the cap off a plastic bottle, then carefully cut the top part off the bottle. Turn the top upside down to make a funnel and tape it into the bottom part.

2. Place your rain gauge outside in an open area so it can catch any rain. (Place stones around your rain gauge to stop it from blowing over.)

3. The next day, measure the depth of any water in the bottle with a ruler. Then, empty the bottle.

	inches
Monday	2.5
Tuesday	1
Wednesday	1.5
Thursday	0
Friday	0.5
Saturday	1
Sunday	1.25

4. Measure the rainfall at the same time every day for a week. Mark your results on a graph, like this.

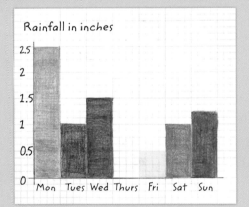

Rainfall in inches

Showing your results in a graph helps you see the way rainfall changes each day. You could continue to record rainfall for several weeks or months if you want to, to see the way it varies over a longer period of time.

Air power

Discover how you can use air to make things move.

223 Make a balloon race car

1. Cut out a square of card stock. Bend up a strip along each side.

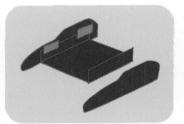

2. Cut out two race car sides. Tape them to the bent-up strips.

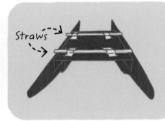

Straws

3. Tape two straws to the underside of the card stock, like this.

Use a kebab stick to make the holes bigger.

4. Use a thumbtack to make a hole in the middle of four plastic bottle tops.

5. Slide kebab sticks through the straws and push a bottle top onto the end of each stick.

6. Roll some card stock into a tube, tape it and slide it into the mouth of a long balloon. Tape the balloon to the tube.

7. Place tape loosely over the tube and stick it to the car. Blow up the balloon, and pinch the tube closed. Then, let go.

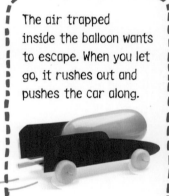

The air trapped inside the balloon wants to escape. When you let go, it rushes out and pushes the car along.

You could make a few cars and race them with your friends.

224 Fluttering bird

1. Cut out a strip of stiff paper, with a curved top. Then, draw a bird at the top of the paper.

2. Fold back a strip at the base to make a flap. Tape it to a table so the paper stands up.

3. Place a bottle in front of the bird. Blow at the bottle. What happens?

The bottle is in the way, but your breath flows around its curved sides onto the paper, making the bird seem to flutter.

225 Air-cushioned disc

1. Stick a thick layer of poster tack around the base of a closed sports bottle cap. Use the tack to fix the cap over the hole on the print side of an old CD or DVD.

"Pull-up" sports cap

2. Blow up a balloon, fit the end snugly over the cap and let go. Put the disc on a smooth surface. Pinch the balloon-covered cap firmly, pull it open, and push the disc forward.

The balloon should stay inflated on the closed cap.

The disc should slide along smoothly. Once the cap is opened, air rushes out of the balloon, through the cap, making a cushion of air under the disc. It glides on this air like a hovercraft, until the balloon is empty.

226 Bobbing ball

1. Cut out a circle of paper. Make a cut into the middle, then overlap the sides to make a cone.

2. Tape the cone together. Snip a small piece off the tip.

Tape the cone inside and out.

3. Slide the short end of a bendy straw into the hole.

4. Use poster tack to fix the straw to the inside of the cone and to fill any gaps.

Poster tack

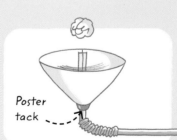

5. Scrunch a piece of foil into a ball and place it in the cone over the end of the straw. Blow into the straw.

Poster tack

As you blow, a stream of air flows under the ball and pushes it up, so it hovers. Air also flows up the sides of the cone to make a cushion of air. When the ball falls onto this air cushion, the ball bounces.

Shadow puppets

Make some shadow puppets and find out more about light and shadows.

227 Shadow hands

1. Shine a bright lamp directly at a wall in a dark room. (Shadows are easier to see on a plain, pale wall.)

2. Put your hands in the position shown below, in front of the light, to make a bird shadow on the wall.

3. You could experiment with hand positions to make other animals, such as a rabbit...

4. ...a deer

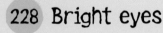

5. ...or an elephant.

Shadows are the absence of light. Light travels in straight lines, so when you hold up your hands in front of the light, you block out the light in the same shape as your hands. This makes the shadow appear.

228 Bright eyes

1. Draw a bat with eyes on a piece of card stock. Cut it out.

2. Make eye holes by pushing a pencil through the card stock. Tape on a straw to make a handle.

3. Hold the bat between a lamp and a wall. Can you see the eyes in its shadow?

The bat shape blocks out the light, but the holes allow light to pass through, creating gaps in the shadow.

229 Snapping crocodile

1. Draw two shapes on card stock for a crocodile's head and lower jaw. Cut them out. Use a pencil to make a hole for its eye.

2. Join the pieces with a paper fastener. Tape a straw to the back of the upper jaw. Tape another straw to the front of the lower jaw.

3. Hold the head between a lamp and a wall. Move the lower jaw rod up and down and watch the shadow.

The shadow head moves at the same time and in the same way as the puppet. This is because the puppet blocks the light in each position it moves through, creating a shadow that does exactly the same.

230 Near and far

1. Place your hand between a lamp and a wall. Move it closer to the lamp. What happens to the shadow?

2. Now move your hand away from the lamp. What happens now?

Light spreads out in straight lines from the lamp. When your hand is close to the lamp, it blocks out a lot of light and the shadow looks big. As you move your hand away, your hand blocks less light, so the shadow shrinks.

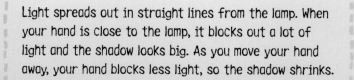

231 Tilted light

1. Point a flashlight straight at a wall, then put your hand in front of the flashlight. What does the shadow look like?

2. Now hold your flashlight at an angle to the wall and put your hand in front of the flashlight again. Is there a difference?

When the light shines at an angle, the shape of the shadow changes and stretches because of the way the light is blocked.

Food science

Discover how some foods change when you mix, freeze or heat them.

232 Whipped cream

It takes 2-3 minutes with an electric beater, or 5 minutes by hand.

You can use the whipped cream in activity 234.

1. Pour a small carton of whipping cream into a bowl. Whisk it with an electric or hand whisk.

2. Whisk the cream until you can make it stand up in soft peaks. How has the cream changed?

After whisking, the cream becomes thicker and more like a solid. Whisking the cream creates air bubbles, which become trapped by fat in the cream. This makes the cream thick and foamy and it fills more space in the bowl.

233 Fluffy egg white

⚠

1. Carefully crack an egg into your hand over a bowl. Open your fingers slightly to let the egg white fall into the bowl. Wash your hands after touching raw egg.

2. Beat the white with an electric or hand whisk until it starts to turn fluffy. Keep beating it until you can make the egg white stand up in soft peaks.

Egg white contains lots of protein. Whisking creates air bubbles and changes the protein so it surrounds the air bubbles, making the egg white expand into a stiff foam.

234 Frozen strawberry cream

½ cup (150ml) whipped cream
½lb (250g) cut-up strawberries
2 drops of vanilla extract
½ tablespoon of lemon juice
2 tablespoons of powdered sugar

1. Mix the ingredients together in a bowl.

2. Pour the mixture into small bowls.

3. Place the bowls in the freezer. Stir the mixture after two hours, then leave it until it is frozen. (You can eat the result.)

Freezing the cream mixture makes it solid. Stirring it while it freezes breaks it up and makes it less hard, so you end up with ice cream.

84

235 Boil an egg

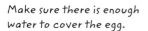

1. Place an egg in a pan of cold water. Put a lid on the pan and heat the water until it starts to boil.

Make sure there is enough water to cover the egg.

2. Turn off the heat and leave the pan for fifteen minutes. Then, place the egg in a bowl of cold water.

3. Tap the egg with a spoon to crack it, then take off the shell. Cut the egg in half and look at it.

As the egg heats up, the yolk and egg white turn from liquid to solid. Eggs contain lots of protein. Heat changes the protein, making it clump together and harden.

236 Making butter

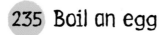

1. Half-fill a jar with whipping cream and put on the lid.

2. Shake the jar for about 10-15 minutes until you see a yellow blob of butter floating in some liquid.

3. Remove the butter from the jar. You can spread it on some bread and eat it if you want to.

Cream contains a lot of fat. When you shake cream, the fat starts to clump together to form butter, which is solid. The liquid left behind – called buttermilk – has very little fat in it.

237 Making plastic from milk

1. Pour a cup of milk into a saucepan. Gently warm the milk until it's hot, but don't let it boil.

2. Turn off the heat. Then, add two tablespoons of vinegar and stir the milk until lumps form.

3. Pour the milk into a fine sieve over the sink.

4. Collect the lumps and press them into different shapes. Leave them to dry on some newspaper for two days. (Don't eat the shapes.)

You could press the lumps into cookie cutters to make different shapes.

Milk contains a kind of protein called casein. When you add vinegar to hot milk, the casein clumps together into rubbery lumps that harden as they dry. Casein can also be turned into hard plastic to make buttons.

Balancing butterflies

Find out about balancing points by making some balancing butterflies.

Balancing points

The balancing point of an object is the single spot on it where it can rest steadily without falling over. This is because the weight of all parts of the object are spread evenly around the balancing point.

238 Make a butterfly

1. Draw a butterfly like this on card stock and cut it out.

2. Tape a coin under each front wing tip.

3. Hold the butterfly so its head is resting on a glass. Can you make it balance?

Coins underneath

You could balance your butterfly on a twig.

The butterfly will balance on its balancing point. The weight of the coins moves the butterfly's balancing point, bringing it forward from its middle to its head.

239 Add more weight

Tape an extra coin to one side of your butterfly. Where does it balance now?

When you add an extra coin, the balancing point moves toward the added weight.

Try balancing your butterfly on the tip of a pencil.

240 Move the weight

Use the butterfly from activity 238, or make another one, and tape one coin under its wing tip and another in the middle. Now try to balance it. Where is the balancing point?

The balancing point wil be between the two coins, where the weight is equal on both sides.

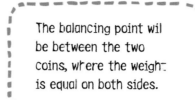

You could experiment with fixing the coins in different positions on the butterfly to see what happens to the balancing point.

241 Pipe-cleaner twist

Bend a pipe cleaner into a tall, flattened "u" shape, then twist it in the middle, like this. Can you balance it on the bottom of a coat hanger?

You can't balance this shape on the wire. The point where the weight is centered is too high above the base, which makes it unstable.

242 Pipe-cleaner dangly

Take the twisted pipe cleaner from activity 241 and bend its sides all the way down, like this. Can you balance it now?

It's easier to balance the pipe cleaner now because the point where its weight is centered is lower than the base. This makes it much more stable.

243 Dangly with beads

Add one or two beads to the ends of the pipe-cleaner dangly from activity 242. What effect does this have?

Adding beads increases the weight lower down. This makes the pipe cleaner more stable.

244 See-saw

Cut out a strip of card stock. Fold it into three and tape the ends to make a triangle. Can you balance a ruler on the point of your triangle?

The ruler balances in the middle, where its weight is equal on both sides.

Moving images

Explore moving images and discover how they can trick your brain.

245 Make a flip book

1. Cut 14 small rectangles of paper, thin enough to see through for tracing. Stack them neatly and staple them at one end.

2. Use a black pen to draw a big square on the last page and fill it in. Then, turn to the page before.

3. Draw a slightly smaller filled-in square on the next page, and an even smaller square on the page after that, and so on.

4. When all the pages are filled, hold the fastened edge and flip through the book, starting at either end. What do you see?

246 Make a moving stick figure

1. Make a book of 14 pages, as in step 1 above. Draw a stick figure on the last page. Trace the figure on the page before, but change its position slightly.

2. Working backward, keep drawing the figure, making tiny changes to its position each time. Then, flip through the book. What happens?

As you flip through the pages, the square appears to grow or shrink gradually. Your eyes and brain blend the drawings together, so you don't notice the turning pages.

Your brain blends the pictures together as it sees the drawings on each page, so the figure appears to move.

Use a sequence of still pictures to make a moving stick figure.

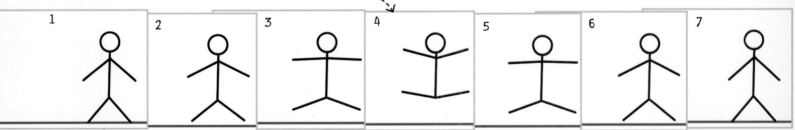

*Each new position should be part of a gradual sequence, like this.**

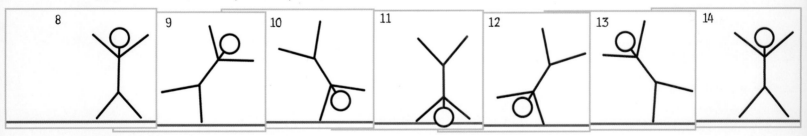

*You could trace these figures or print them out from the Usborne Quicklinks website at www.usborne.com/quicklinks

247 Spider web

Use plain card stock.

Use a hole punch to make two holes on each side of the circle.

1. Draw around a mug on a piece of card stock and cut out the circle.

2. Draw a web on one side of the card stock and a spider on the other.

3. Make two pairs of holes. Thread some string through each pair.

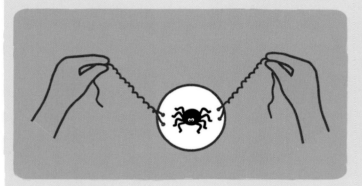

4. Hold the string and flip the circle over and over, until the string is twisted tightly.

5. Then, pull the string tight with both hands. What do you see?

As the circle spins, your eyes see one picture after the other in quick succession. It happens so quickly that your brain can't separate the pictures, so the spider looks as if it is on the web.

248 Make a magic spinner

1. Draw around a mug on a piece of card stock and cut out the circle. Use a pencil and ruler to divide the circle into eight.

2. Use markers to color the sections. Fill three sections in red, three in green and two in blue, like this.

3. Push a pencil halfway through the circle. Hold the pencil between your palms and twist it as fast as you can. What do you see?

The circle spins so quickly that your brain can't separate out the different colors. Instead, they seem to merge into each other to make white or pale gray.

Testing acids and bases

All substances are acids, bases (the opposite of acids), or neutral. You can use red cabbage to make a color-changing liquid called an indicator to find out if liquids are acids, bases, or neither.

249 Red cabbage indicator

Red cabbage

Red cabbage contains a purple substance that changes color when it is mixed with acids or bases. Acids turn the pigment red, while bases turn it blue or green.

1. Put some chopped red cabbage in a heatproof bowl, then carefully pour just-boiled water over the top.

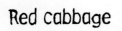

2. Leave the mixture for 10 minutes, then use a sieve to separate the liquid and the cabbage.

3. Put a spoonful of the indicator liquid into another bowl and add a spoonful of vinegar. What happens?

Your cabbage water should start out purple.

Cabbage water and vinegar

Vinegar turns the indicator red because it is an acid.

250 Lemon juice

Put a spoonful of red cabbage indicator into a bowl and add a spoonful of lemon juice. What happens this time?

Mixing lemon juice with the indicator turns it red, which means lemon juice is an acid.

Cabbage water and lemon juice

251 Baking soda

Mix a little baking soda with a spoonful of red cabbage indicator in a bowl. What color do you get?

Baking soda turns the liquid blue (or blue-green), showing that baking soda is a base.

Cabbage water and baking soda

252 Milk of magnesia

Try the experiment using a spoonful of the indicator and a spoonful of milk of magnesia. (You can buy this from pharmacies.)

Milk of magnesia turns the indicator green, showing it is a weak base.

Cabbage water and milk of magnesia

254 Water

Add a spoonful of water to a spoonful of the indicator. Does anything happen?

Cabbage water and tap water

Pure water is neutral. Tap water often has traces of other things in it, but they are usually too weak to change the indicator — so nothing happens.

253 Base to acid

1. Pour a little indicator into a bowl and add enough baking soda to make it change color.

2. Then, add some vinegar. Keep adding vinegar. Can you make the color change back again?

When vinegar mixes with baking soda, it fizzes up. (See pages 10-11 to find out more.)

The base (baking soda) turns the indicator blue or green. If you add enough acid (vinegar), you can change the color through purple, until it is red.

255 Cola cleaning

1. Pour some cola into a glass and drop a dirty copper coin into it.

2. Remove the coin the next day. What does it look like now?

Over time, copper coins become covered in a dull layer of copper oxide, which is a base. The acid in cola removes the base, leaving the metal looking shiny and new.

Test your senses

Everyone has five senses – taste, smell, sight, hearing and touch. Do these experiments to find out more about how the senses work.

256 Taste and smell

1. Carefully cut and peel a piece of apple and a piece of firm pear. Make them the same size and shape.

2. Close your eyes and hold your nose. Mix up the pieces, then eat one. Which do you think it is?

3. Now eat the other piece. Can you tell if it is apple or pear?

Our sense of smell is a big part of what things taste like. It is much harder to taste individual flavors, such as apple and pear, if you can't smell them.

257 Four basic tastes

1. Take four small bowls. In different bowls, put a spoonful of lemon juice, soy sauce, cold black coffee and sugary water.

2. Close your eyes and hold your nose. Pull a bowl toward you. Dip your finger in and taste the liquid.

3. Now try it again with the other three liquids. Can you taste the difference between them?

You can easily recognize different basic tastes, such as sweet, sour, salty and bitter, even when you can't smell.

258 One eye or two?

1. Hold a pencil with an eraser on the end in each hand, with the erasers pointing inward.

2. Close one eye and try to touch the two erasers together. Can you do it?

3. Now open both eyes and try it again. Is it easier this time?

You will probably find it hard to make the erasers touch with one eye closed. Two eyes give you a better sense of how far away things are, so it is easier to judge the position of the erasers.

259 What can you hear?

When you take away your sense of sight, you usually find you can tune in better to your sense of hearing. So you hear sounds you might not have noticed with your eyes open.

1. Sit inside by an open window. Listen to the sounds from outside. What can you hear?

2. Now close your eyes and listen again. Can you hear more things this time?

260 Touch

1. Bend a paper clip into a 'U' shape. Close your eyes and ask a friend to press either one tip or two gently against the palm of your hand...

2. ...your forehead...

3. ...and your upper arm.

Can you feel how many ends are touching you in each place?

261 Touch test

Collect a variety of objects, such as a tennis ball, a sponge, a pine cone and an apple. Shut your eyes and ask a friend to pass one to you. Can you guess what it is just by feeling it?

Some parts of your body are more sensitive to touch than others. That's because they have more touch sensors. The palms of your hands have a lot of sensors, so you can feel both ends of the paper clip. Your upper arm doesn't have as many, so you may not be able to tell if one end or two are touching your skin.

The shape and texture of some objects make them easier to identify by touch than others.

Turning power

Learn how you can use water and stored energy to provide power to move things.

262 Make a water wheel

1. Collect eight empty yogurt cartons. Place a carton with its mouth at the edge of a paper plate and staple it to the plate.

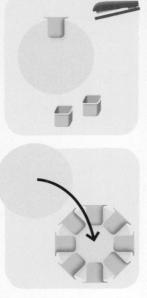

2. Staple the other cartons all the way around the plate, like this. Staple another plate onto the other side of the cartons.

3. Use a thumbtack to carefully make a hole in the middle of each plate. Push a kebab stick through the holes and balance the wheel over a bucket.

4. Place the bucket in a bathtub, or outside. Using a pitcher or hose, pour water down one side of the wheel and keep pouring. What happens?

As water fills each carton, that carton gets heavier and drops down, making the wheel turn. The wheel will keep turning as long as the water keeps pouring.

You could use circles of card stock instead of paper plates. This water wheel has a layer of decorated paper covering the stapled cardboard.

263 Reverse water wheel

Now, start pouring water down the other side of the wheel. What happens this time?

By pouring water down the other side of the wheel, you make it change direction, so it turns the other way.

264 Make a rubber-band motor

1. Thread a rubber band through a spool of thread. Slide a popsicle stick through one end of the band and tape it down.

2. Stand the spool up, so it rests on the popsicle stick with the rubber band loop sticking out of the top.

3. Slide another popsicle stick through the empty loop and wind the band tight. Then, et go and see what happens.

Motors make things spin to create movement. As you twist the rubber band, you are storing up energy. When you let go, this energy is released and the band unwinds, making the spool spin around quickly.

265 Make a bathtub torpedo

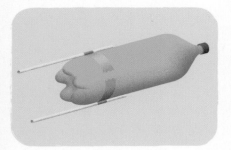

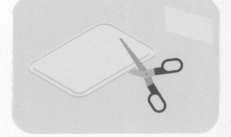

1. Use packing tape to stick a straw to either side of a large plastic bottle, like this. (Keep the cap on the bottle.)

2. Carefully cut two rectangles of stiff plastic from the lid of a plastic tub. They should be almost as wide as the bottle.

3. Cut a slit in each rectangle, halfway along, like this. Then, carefully slot the rectangles together to make a paddle.

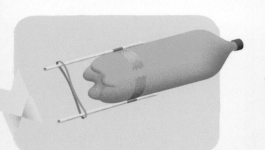

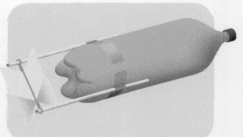

4. Slip a rubber band over the ends of the straws. Put the paddle inside the band and turn it around and around to wind it up.

5. Hold the paddle in place and put the bottle in a half-full bathtub. Let go. What does it do?

As you turn the paddle, the rubber band becomes twisted, storing up energy. When you let go, the band unwinds and the energy is released, making the paddle turn. This pushes the bottle through the water, like a torpedo.

Reflexes and reactions

Test your body's reactions, and discover reflexes – the instant, automatic reactions that can help protect you from danger.

You'll need a friend or a group of friends for these activities.

266 Eye spy

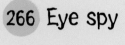

This works best in daytime.

1. Stand by a mirror in a well-lit room and look closely at your eyes. Then, close your eyes and count to thirty.

2. Now open your eyes quickly and watch them closely. Do you notice a change?

> The black parts of your eyes (called pupils) should get bigger, but quickly return to normal. This is because your eyes react to light. If it is bright, your pupils shrink to protect your eyes from too much light. If it is dark (or your eyes close), your pupils relax and open wide to let in as much light as possible to help you see in the gloom.

267 Sudden noise

Ask a friend to read this book while you prepare to test his reflexes. Walk quietly behind him, then suddenly clap your hands. What happens?

CLAP!

> A sudden clap is likely to startle your friend and trigger a reflex, probably making him jump, shout or turn to look at you.

268 Blink test

1. Ask a friend to stand on the other side of a window or glass door from you.

2. Ask him to stare at you. Then, quickly throw a ball of paper or rolled-up tissue at the glass.

Your friend

You

> Your friend's eyes should shut automatically to protect them from harm, even though he knows the glass will stop anything from hitting his face.

269 Heart rate

1. Ask a friend to put one hand on his chest and count how many times his heart beats in one minute.

2. Then, ask him to close his eyes. Clap your hands suddenly behind him. Ask him to count his heart rate again. Is there a difference?

> Your friend's heart rate should be faster after the clap. When you're surprised, a reflex makes your heart beat more quickly. A special substance called adrenalin is pumped around your body, too, making you ready to run away in case of danger.

270 Think fast

Stand in a circle of four or five people. Call someone's name and throw a ball toward that person. Does he or she react in time to catch it? Ask that person to do the same to another person in the circle, and so on. What happens if you do it faster and faster?

FRED!

> This game tests how quickly people react to hearing their names. This is not a reflex – it needs a moment's thought, so it's a reaction. Some people will react quickly and catch the ball easily, while others will be slower and might not catch it at all.

271 Snappy snap

Play a game of snap with a friend. You should each have half a pack of cards. Take turns placing one card on the table, face up in a pile. Whenever a matching pair of cards appears, the person who is fastest to shout *Snap!* and slap a hand down on the pile wins all those cards.

> Snap tests how quickly you react to seeing a matching pair, and how well your eyes and hands work together. This is known as hand–eye coordination. It gets better with practice. So playing more snap should improve your results – just as practicing music, sports or video games improves your performance.

272 Ruler drop

1. Hold up a long ruler. Ask a friend to place her hand just below it, ready to catch it.

Have the zero at the bottom. --->

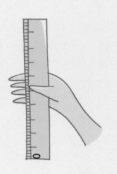

2. Suddenly let go. Can your friend grab the ruler before it reaches the floor? Where on the ruler do her fingers end up?

3. You could test several people and compare their reactions by seeing where on the ruler their fingers land.

NAME	MEASUREMENT
Gary	Miss
Asha	2in (5cm)
Ryan	1.5in (4cm)
Poppy	4in (10cm)

> This test measures reaction times. The faster the reaction, the closer to the zero mark a person will catch the ruler. The slower the reaction, the higher the measurement on the ruler will be.

Bending light

Discover how you can bend light by making it pass through different substances – an effect known as refraction.

273 Split ruler

Fill a glass with water and lower a ruler into it. Look at the ruler through the side of the glass. What happens? Place a straw in the glass, too. Does the same thing happen?

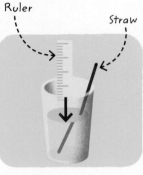

Ruler

Straw

When you look at something, what you really see is the light bouncing off it. Light bends as it travels from air to water. So when you look at the ruler and straw in the glass, they appear to bend where they enter the water.

This photo shows a ruler, straw and pencil all appearing to bend at the water's surface, where the air and water meet.

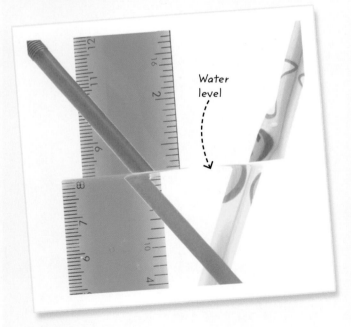

Water level

274 Broken spoon

1. Half-fill a jar with water and top it up with cooking oil.

2. Lower a tall spoon into the liquids. What happens? What can you see if you use a straw?

A square jar will work best.

Light bends as it passes from air into oil, and again when it passes into water. This makes it look as though the spoon and the straw are broken in two places.

The spoon and straws seem to break where the air meets the oil, then bend again where the oil meets the water.

275 Reappearing coin

1. Use poster tack to stick a coin in the middle of a shallow bowl.

2. Step back from the bowl until you can't see the coin any more.

3. Slowly pour water into the bowl until you see the coin reappear.

The coin doesn't move. But when you add water, the light bouncing off the coin has to pass through both water and air. This makes the light bend over the edge of the bowl at a different angle, allowing you to see the coin again.

276 Disappearing stamp

1. Place a stamp on a flat surface. Put a glass jar with a lid over the stamp. You should still be able to see the stamp through the jar.

2. Fill the jar with water. Put on the lid and put the jar back over the stamp. Can you see it from any angle now?

The water in the jar makes the light from the stamp bend so much that you can't see the stamp from the side. Once the lid is on, you can't see the stamp from above either.

277 Magnifying water drops

1. Place a sheet of clear plastic over some writing in this book.

2. Dip a straw into a glass of water. Then, put one finger over the top to keep the water inside the straw.

3. Move the straw over the plastic and lift your finger to release a few drops. Does the writing look different through the drops?

Light bends and spreads out as it passes through the drop of water, making the writing appear larger. A magnifying glass works in the same way.

278 Arrow flip

1. Draw a horizontal arrow on a piece of card stock. Fill a glass with water. Place the card stock behind it and look at the arrow through the water.

2. Try twisting the glass and moving the card stock farther away from the glass. What do you notice?

Watch the arrow as it goes behind the glass.

At a certain point behind the glass, the arrow will appear to flip and point the other way. This happens because of the way the light bends.

Floating and sinking

Try these experiments to learn more about why different things float and sink.

279 Make a floating jellyfish

1. Cut a large square out of a thin plastic bag.

2. Find the middle of the square. Tie some string loosely around it.

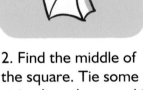

3. Make lots of cuts in the plastic below the string, like this.

4. Turn the plastic over. Pour a little water into the middle, leaving some space for air. Tighten the string.

5. Fill a plastic bottle with water and carefully push the plastic bag 'jellyfish' inside. What happens?

6. Screw on the lid, then turn the bottle upside-down and watch what happens.

Air rises in water. When you put your jellyfish into water, the air trapped inside it rises up, making the jellyfish float up to the top.

280 Make a floating fish

1. Carefully cut a little fish out of thin, stiff plastic. Attach it to a paper clip using poster tack.

Make a fish that's small enough to fit inside a plastic bottle.

3. Fill a plastic bottle with water and place the fish inside. Screw on the bottle cap.

2. Cover the holes in a pen lid with poster tack, leaving the bottom open. Attach the paper clip to the lid with more tack.

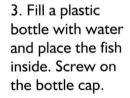

4. Squeeze the bottle. What happens to the fish? Let go again. What happens now?

When you put the fish in the water, an air bubble becomes trapped inside the pen lid, making the fish float.

Squeezing the bottle squashes the air bubble and lets more water into the pen lid, making the fish sink.

When you stop squeezing, the air bubble returns to its normal size, pushing the water out. This makes the fish float up to the top again.

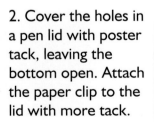

281 Orange peel

1. Place an orange in a pitcher of water. Does the orange float or sink?

2. Peel the orange and put it back in the pitcher. What happens now?

Orange skin has lots of tiny air pockets in it, making the orange float. Without the skin, the orange sinks.

282 Bobbing raisins

Pour some sparkling water into a glass, then sprinkle in a few raisins. What happens to them?

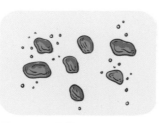

At first the raisins sink. But sparkling water contains bubbles of gas, which stick to the raisins and make them float up to the surface. There the gas escapes, leaving them to sink again.

283 Salty water

Carefully lower a fresh egg into a bowl of water. Does it sink or float? Remove the egg and stir in several heaped spoonfuls of salt. Put the egg back. What happens now?

Eggs are more dense than water (which means that an egg-sized amount of water weighs less than an egg), so they sink. But adding salt makes the water denser than the egg, so the egg floats in salty water.

284 Make a carrot submarine

1. Take a small length of carrot and slice one side so it is flat.

2. Use a screwdriver to make a hole in the carrot, halfway along the flat side.

Make sure the hole doesn't go all the way through.

3. Place the carrot in a bowl of water, flat side down. Push toothpicks into it until it sinks.

4. Remove the carrot from the water and pack the hole with baking powder.

5. Put the carrot back into the water, flat side down. You should see it sink and rise, over and over.

The toothpicks make the carrot too heavy to float. When baking powder is added, it reacts with the water to produce bubbles of carbon dioxide gas underneath the carrot. These bubbles make the carrot float up to the surface, where they burst, leaving the carrot to sink down again. This continues until all the baking powder is used up.

Simple machines

In science, a machine is a tool that makes lifting, pushing, pulling or turning easier to do. Find out how to make some machines and discover how they work.

285 Make some gears

Make sure the teeth interlock.

1. Lay a piece of thin paper over this page and trace the big gear. Move the paper a little, then trace the small gear.*

2. Glue the paper gear shapes onto a piece from a cardboard box. Carefully cut out both gears.

3. On another piece of cardboard, fit the gears side-by-side, like this. Push a thumbtack into the middle of each one.

4. Use your finger to turn the big gear clockwise. Which way does the small gear turn?

Alternatively, you could print out a template from the Usborne Quicklinks website at www.usborne.com/quicklinks.

Small gear

You could glue on a small lid to make a handle for turning.

Cut the teeth as neatly as possible.

The small gear turns counterclockwise, which is the opposite direction of the big gear.

Big gear

You could try making a medium gear and see how it turns, too.

Medium gear

286 Turning speed

Turn the big gear slowly all the way around once. Does the small gear turn at the same speed?

Mark a dot on one tooth and turn the gear until this tooth is in the same position again.

The smaller gear turns faster than the big gear and completes more turns for every full turn of the big gear.

287 How many teeth?

Count the number of teeth on each gear. Does the number of teeth affect the speed?

The speed of each gear depends on the number of teeth. If the big gear has twice as many teeth, the small gear will turn twice for every single turn of the big gear.

288 Make a lever

1. Fold a strip of strong card stock into three to make a triangular tube, and tape together the edges.

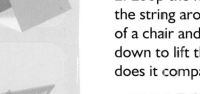

2. Place a ruler on your tube, and place a small, heavy object on one end.

3. Push the other end of the ruler down to lift the object.

4. Move the triangle along the ruler and push again. Which position makes it easiest to lift the object?

The ruler acts as a lever – a long stick that helps you move or lift something.

When the triangle is close to the object, the lever moves farther, but it's easier to push.

Easier to push

When the triangle is farther from the object, the lever moves less far, but you have to push it harder.

Harder to push

289 Make a fixed pulley

1. Tie a piece of string around a book, leaving a long loose end. Try lifting the book with the string.

2. Loop the loose end of the string around the back of a chair and pull the string down to lift the book. How does it compare?

The back of the chair acts as a fixed pulley, which changes the pulling direction so you pull down instead of up. This is easier because you can use your body weight to help lift the book.

290 Moving pulley system

1. Thread an empty spool onto a wooden skewer and hang up the skewer with string. Thread more string through a second spool and tie the ends to a small, heavy toy.

2. Tie one end of a long piece of string to your hanging point. Loop the other end under the toy's reel and over the hanging reel. Pull the loose end. Is it easier to lift the toy than it was using the fixed pulley?

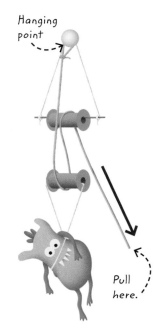

Hanging point

Pull here.

The reels act as pulleys, and the bottom reel is free to move. The two strings that support the lower reel divide the toy's weight, so you need only pull with a force equal to half the toy's weight, but you pull the string twice as far as the toy moves. So lifting with this pulley system needs less effort, but you must pull the string farther than with a fixed pulley.

Bouncing light

See how light bounces off shiny things and use this to create repeating patterns.

291 Make a kaleidoscope

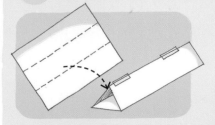

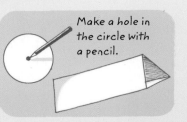

Make a hole in the circle with a pencil.

1. Glue some shiny foil onto a postcard. Fold the card in three lengthways, with the foil inside. Tape the edges to make a triangular tube.

2. Cut a circle of thick paper, big enough to cover one end of the tube. Fold the sides of the circle over one end of the tube and tape them in place.

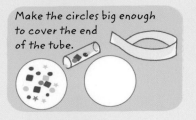

Make the circles big enough to cover the end of the tube.

3. Cut two circles of tracing paper. Sprinkle sequins or glitter on one circle, tape them together and tape them over the other end of the tube.

4. Put your eye to the hole, face a window and turn the tube around. What do you see? Keep turning the tube and see what happens.

Light bouncing off shiny things is called reflection. As rays of light enter the tube, they bounce off the shiny sequins and off the shiny foil to create lots of colorful reflection patterns.

292 Pattern tube

Remove the sequin circles from the tube you made for 291. Use markers to draw bright swirls on a new circle of tracing paper. Tape it over the end and look through the hole to see some more colorful patterns.

Light bounces off the swirls onto the foil. The surface of the foil is uneven, so it reflects the parts of the pattern at different angles, making the colors blur together.

293 Glitter art

Glue lots of glitter to a picture cut from a magazine. Shine a flashlight at it and twist the picture in the light. Do the sparkles change?

As the picture moves, rays of light bounce off the shiny glitter at different angles, making the picture sparkle in different ways.

294 Mirror magic

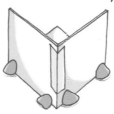
You can add tape to hold the mirrors more firmly.

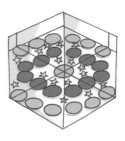

1. Take three small, square mirrors. Use poster tack to stick one mirror onto a flat surface.

2. Use more poster tack to stand the other two mirrors up alongside the flat one, like this.

3. Arrange tiny, bright items such as beads, glitter or scraps of paper on the bottom mirror. What do you see?

The arrangement you create is repeated again and again as each mirror reflects it.

These are the types of patterns you can create in activity 294. Use different objects to make different patterns.

295 Wall of mirrors

Arrange three small mirrors in a triangle, like this. You can hold them, tape them or use poster tack to hold them in place. Put an object in the middle of the triangle and peek inside. What do you see?

The reflections seem to go on forever, as each mirror reflects the images from the others.

Making bubbles

Make your own bubble mix and use it to learn how bubbles are formed.

296 Big bubbles

1. Bend a long piece of wire into a circle, small enough to fit inside a tray. Twist the ends of the wire together to make a handle. This will be your bubble wand.

2. Make some bubble mix (see above, right) and pour it into a tray. Dip the wand into the liquid...

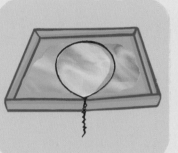

3. ...and wave it slowly through the air to make a big bubble.

The bubble mix forms a stretchy 'skin' over the wire. When you wave or blow air into it, the skin stretches and traps some air inside it, making a bubble.

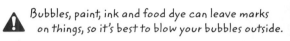

How to make bubble mix

Gently mix half a cup of dishwashing liquid, two cups of water and two teaspoons of sugar in a pitcher. Use this mix for all the activities on these pages.

⚠ Bubbles, paint, ink and food dye can leave marks on things, so it's best to blow your bubbles outside.

297 Make a square wand

Take another piece of wire and make a square wand. Dip it in a tray of bubble mix, then wave it through the air. What happens?

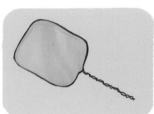

298 Bubbles from a bottle

1. Carefully cut the end off a plastic bottle.

2. Dip the cut end in a tray of bubble mix. Then, take it out again.

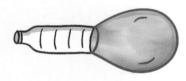

Keep blowing until your bubble bursts.

3. Blow through the neck of the bottle to make a bubble.

No matter what shape your wand is, bubbles are always round. This is because the stretchy skin always wants to pull back into the smallest possible shape – a sphere.

299 Colorful sock bubbles

Stir in the dye.

Blow here.

Lie the paper on a tray.

1. Take an old sock and stretch it over the wide end of the cut-off bottle from activity 298.

2. Add some food dye to some bubble mix in a bowl. Dip the sock-covered end in the mix.

3. Hold the sock-covered end over a piece of paper. Blow through the neck of the bottle. What happens?

As you blow, the bubble mix passes through lots of tiny holes in the sock, making small colorful bubbles that cling together. As the bubbles burst, they leave bubble shaped patterns of dye on the paper.

This bubble picture was made by printing several times on the same piece of paper, using different colored bubble mix.

300 Make bubble pictures

1. Half-fill a tray with bubble mix and squeeze in some poster paint or ink. Stir it all together.

2. Take a straw and gently blow into the mixture to make lots of bubbles. Stop when the bubbles are just above the rim.

3. Place a piece of paper on top of the bubbles, then lift it up. You should get a colorful print.

Moving things

Explore how things move and how moving things want to keep on moving.

301 Make a jumping bean

1. Cut out a rectangular piece of foil and roll it around a glue stick or big pen to make a tube that's wide enough to fit a marble inside.

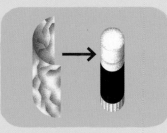

2. Carefully remove the tube and fold over one end. Place a marble inside the tube, then fold over the other end, too.

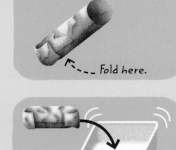

Fold here.

3. Put the tube in a plastic food storage box. Shake the box until the ends of the tube are round and smooth, like a bean.

4. Place the bean in your hand and tip your hand gently one way, then another. What happens?

The bean jumps around as if there were a live bug inside. Once an object has begun to move, it wants to continue moving in the same direction. This is known as momentum. As your hand tips the foil tube, the marble starts to roll. When it hits the end of the tube, it makes the tube flip over so it can keep on rolling.

302 Marble in a pan

Place a marble in a saucepan. Swirl the pan in a circle until the marble is whizzing around the inside. Now stop moving the pan. What happens?

The marble continues to roll around the inside of the pan. This is because it has momentum.

303 Spinning coin

Push a coin into a balloon, then blow up the balloon. Whirl the balloon around as fast as you can, so the coin whizzes around the inside. Then, stop moving the balloon. What happens?

Momentum makes the coin continue to whiz around the inside of the balloon, even when you've stopped moving the balloon.

304 Swirling water

Stir a glass of water in rapid circular movements. Then, stop stirring and take out the spoon. What happens?

When you stop stirring, the momentum of the water makes it continue swirling around in the same direction.

305 Marble collision

Tape two rulers to a table, the width of a marble apart. Place a marble between the rulers, halfway down, then roll another marble so it hits the first. What happens?

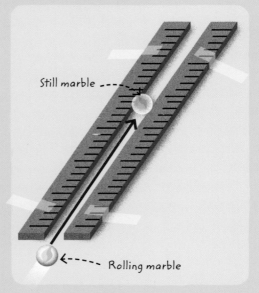

Still marble

Rolling marble

When the marbles collide, the momentum from the rolling marble transfers to the still one. The rolling marble stops and the still marble starts moving.

306 Three marbles

Place two marbles between the rulers, halfway down. The marbles should be touching, but not moving. Roll a third marble at them and watch what happens.

This time when the marbles collide, the momentum from the rolling marble passes through the middle marble to the one on the end. So the rolling marble stops, the middle marble stays put, and the end marble starts to roll.

307 Spinning egg

1. Place an uncooked egg on a table and gently start spinning it on its side.

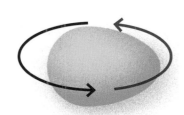

2. Touch it briefly with your finger to stop it from moving, then pull your finger away. What happens?

When you touch the egg, it stops spinning for a moment, then starts spinning again. The egg is liquid inside, and the liquid has enough momentum to make the egg start moving again.

308 Still egg

Repeat activity 307 with a hard-boiled egg. What happens this time?

The hard-boiled egg stops spinning. It is solid inside. So when you stop it, you stop the whole egg from moving, not just the shell.

309 Marble bowling game

1. This is a game for two or more players. Each player puts a marble on a hard floor.

Player 1

Player 2

Player 3

2. Place another marble on the floor a short distance away. This is the target.

Target

3. Players take turns to roll their marbles at the target. The object is to hit the target and end up as close to it as possible.

If you hit the target, the momentum from the rolling marble passes into it and makes it move away. The faster the rolling marble moves, the more momentum is created and the farther the target moves. To win, you need to roll your marble just fast enough to hit the target, without sending it flying.

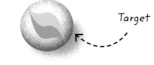

Water resistance

Find out how water stays on some surfaces, but runs off others – an effect known as water resistance.

310 Wax and watery paint

Use a wax crayon to draw some shapes on thick, white paper. Then, brush thin, watery paint over the top. What happens?

The watery paint runs off the crayon because wax is water resistant. Paint sticks to the paper because paper is absorbent.

311 Using thick paint

Try painting again over the shapes you made in 310, this time with thick paint. What happens now?

Thick paint contains less water and more color, so it runs off less easily and can still cover the crayon.

312 Iron-on wax crayon

1. Make some crayon shavings using a cheese grater. Sprinkle them over a piece of thick paper.

2. Lay some baking parchment on top and carefully iron over it for a few seconds.

3. Peel off the baking parchment, then paint over the crayon with watery paint. What do you see?

Don't grate your fingers!

Put the iron on the lowest setting and ask an adult to help.

In some places you may see white wax separating from the color in the crayon.

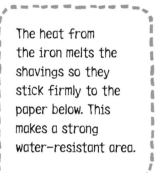
The heat from the iron melts the shavings so they stick firmly to the paper below. This makes a strong water-resistant area.

313 Margarine

Put a teaspoon of margarine or butter on a plate. Dip a finger in it and make some fingerprints on paper. Brush over the paper with watery paint. What happens?

Candles, margarine, butter, lip balm and petroleum jelly are made from wax, fats or oils, and they all resist watery paint in similar ways. Soap doesn't resist watery paint. Although it is made from oils and fatty products, it also has ingredients in it that help it mix and foam up in water.

314 Candle

Draw a shape on some paper with a candle, then paint over it with watery paint and see what you notice.

Press firmly with the candle.

315 Lip balm

Dip a finger into some lip balm or petroleum jelly and draw something on a piece of paper. Then, paint over the top. What do you see?

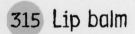

316 Soap

Use a piece of soap to draw a shape on some paper, then paint over it. What do you notice this time?

111

Catapults

Catapults are machines that are used to throw objects a long way. Find out how they work by storing and releasing energy.

317 Make a cardboard catapult

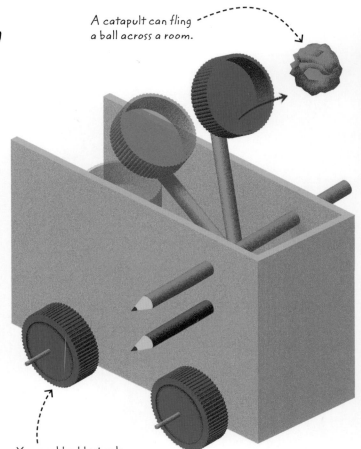

A catapult can fling a ball across a room.

Trim here.

1. Cut the bottom third off a cereal box, like this. Then, trim one of the short sides so it is lower than the others.

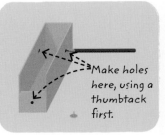

Make holes here, using a thumbtack first.

2. Push a sharp pencil all the way through the box to make a pair of holes. Make another hole in the middle of the low side.

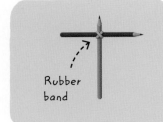

Rubber band

3. To make the catapult arm, make a cross out of two pencils and loop a rubber band around them to hold them in place.

4. Tape a shallow, plastic bottle lid to the bottom of the cross. Cut a rubber band and tie one end of it to the top of the cross.

You could add wheels made from wooden skewers pushed through soft plastic bottle lids. (Make a hole with a thumbtack first.)

When you pull back the catapult arm, the rubber band stores up energy. When you let go, the stored energy is released and transferred to the ball, making it fly through the air.

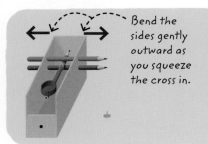

Bend the sides gently outward as you squeeze the cross in.

5. Fit the arms of the cross into the pair of holes you made. Push a sharp pencil all the way through the box above them and leave it there.

The low side means you can pull the catapult back farther.

Piece of straw

6. Push the end of the cut rubber band through the hole in the low side and pull it tight. Tie the end around a piece of drinking straw.

7. Make some balls of crumpled paper. Pull back the bottle lid, place a ball on top and let go.

318 Clothespin catapult

Balance a crumpled paper ball on the top end of a clothespin. Press down on the clothespin, then let go.

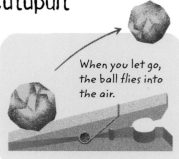

When you let go, the ball *flies* into the air.

319 Hole punch and spoon

Tape a plastic spoon to the top of a hole punch, like this. Load the spoon with a paper ball, press down on the hole punch and let go.

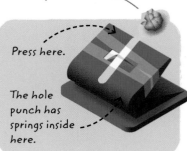

Press here.

The hole punch has springs inside here.

Power to fling the ball comes from energy stored in the squeezed springs of the clothespin and the hole punch.

320 Popsicle sticks and eraser

1. Place an eraser between two popsicle sticks or cardboard nail files.

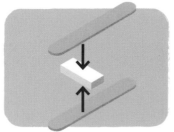

2. Wind a rubber band around the sticks and eraser, like this. Loop another band around the ends of the sticks.

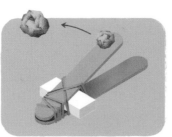

Loop the second band here.

3. Place a ball of paper on the top stick, press down on the stick, then release it. See how far you can fire the ball.

This catapult's firing power comes from energy stored in the bent stick and the stretched rubber bands.

321 Rubber-band finger flinger

Place a rubber band around a finger or thumb. Hold a paper ball at the other end of the rubber band, pull it back and let go.

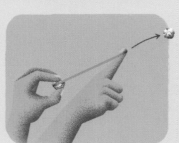

When you let go, the energy stored in the stretched rubber band is transferred to the ball, making it fly through the air. The farther you stretch the band, the more energy it stores and the farther the ball will travel.

322 Crossed-pencils catapult

1. Cross two pencils, like this. Then loop a rubber band around them to hold them in place.

2. Cut a long, strong rubber band and tie the ends onto the cross. Hold a paper ball inside the rubber band, pull it back and let go.

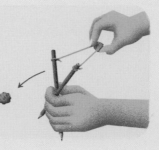

Water power

Do these activities to discover the power of flowing water and find out what you can do with it.

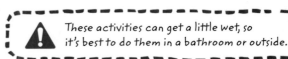
These activities can get a little wet, so it's best to do them in a bathroom or outside.

323 Make a water-powered boat

1. Glue a paper cup to the middle of a thin plastic food box. Push a pencil through the box and into the cup.

2. Take out the pencil and push a long, bendy straw through the holes and tape it in place.

3. Place the boat gently on cold water in a bathtub or sink. Pour water into the cup and watch what happens.

Use a thumbtack to make the holes.

Bendy part

Point the bendy part of the straw down.

The water flows out of the cup through the straw at the back of the boat and into the water below. As it does so, it pushes the boat in the opposite direction, so the boat moves forward.

You could stand a straw in poster tack to make a mast and add paper sails.

You could cut out two boat shapes from a piece of card stock and tape them to the sides of your plastic box if you like.

324 Bottle fountain

1. Use a thumbtack to make three holes near the base of a plastic bottle. Then, use a sharp pencil to make the holes bigger.

2. Stick tape over the holes. Fill the bottle with water and put it on the side of a sink or bathtub.

3. Remove the tape and watch the water flow out. Do you notice anything?

The water spurts most strongly out of the bottom hole because there is more water above pushing down. This is why dams need to be stronger and wider at the bottom than near the top.

325 Bag fountain

Snip some small holes in a plastic bag and hold it over a sink or bathtub. Use a pitcher to pour water into the bag. What happens if you fill the bag and squeeze it?

At first, the water flows out gently. But when you squeeze the bag, you force it out faster.

326 Standing water

1. Use a thumbtack and a sharp pencil to make a hole near the bottom of a small plastic bottle. Cover the hole with tape.

2. Fill the bottle with water and screw on the lid. Remove the tape. What happens? Then, remove the lid. What happens now?

At first when you remove the tape, nothing happens. The water can't flow out at the bottom because no air can flow in at the top to replace it. But when you open the bottle, the air and water can both flow, so now the water rushes out.

327 Water spinner

 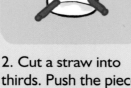

Space the three holes evenly, near the base.

1. Cut the bottom off a large plastic bottle. Use a thumbtack and a pencil to make three holes.

2. Cut a straw into thirds. Push the pieces into the holes. Tape them firmly in place.

3. Make three more holes, thread some string through and tie the ends together. Hold the bottle over a bathtub and pour a pitcher of water into it. What happens?

Make the holes near the top.

As water rushes out through the straws (pushed down by the pressure of water above the hole), the bottle tries to move in the other direction, making it spin.

328 Water squirter

Fold

Don't cut here.

1. Fold a piece of card stock in half. Draw an elephant along the fold.

2. Cut out the elephant, being careful not to cut the fold.

Attach the balloon here.

3. Open the card stock. Then, tape a bendy straw inside, with the bent part lying along the trunk, like this.

4. Half-fill a balloon with water and tape the mouth of the balloon onto the tail end of the straw.

5. Stand the elephant up and squeeze the balloon. What happens?

When you squeeze the balloon, there is less room inside it. So some water gets pushed into the straw and squirts out of the end.

Paper helicopters

Make some paper helicopters and discover how air pushing against their wings makes them spin.

329 Make a cut-paper helicopter

1. Cut a rectangle of paper, twice as long as it is wide. Cut two slits halfway down.

Make each slit one third of the width.

2. Fold in the two sides below the cuts, like this, to make a strip.

3. Fold up the end of the strip and secure it with a paper clip. Then, cut a slit down the top, stopping before the middle.

4. Fold one part of the top to the front, and the other to the back, like this. Hold your helicopter up high and let go. What happens?

— Blades —

Air   Air

As the helicopter falls, air pushes against its blades (wings), making them turn in opposite directions. This makes the helicopter spin. A helicopter with shorter blades spins and falls faster. A helicopter with longer blades stays in the air longer.

Natural spinners

Have you ever seen a maple key rotating in the air? Its helicopter-style wings make it spin, so it can stay in the air longer. This makes it more likely to reach a good spot (away from its parent tree) to grow.

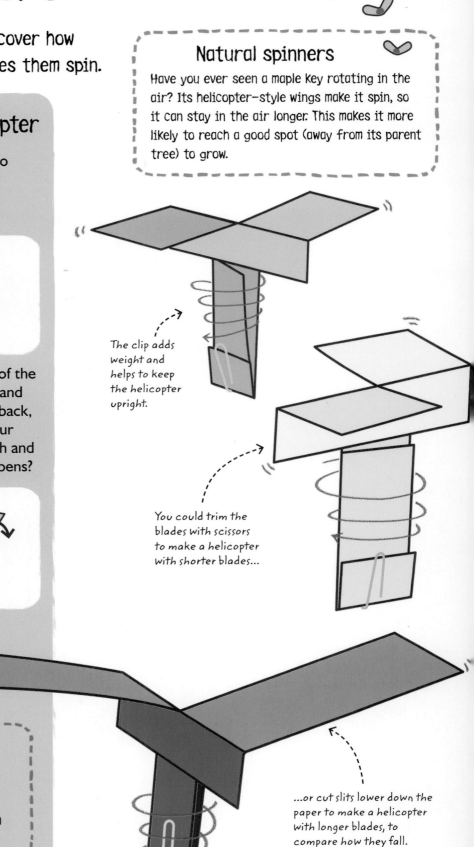

The clip adds weight and helps to keep the helicopter upright.

You could trim the blades with scissors to make a helicopter with shorter blades...

...or cut slits lower down the paper to make a helicopter with longer blades, to compare how they fall.

330 Simple strip helicopter

1. Cut a long strip of paper and fold it in half. Fold up the folded end again and hold it in place with a paper clip.

2. Fold one blade down to the right and the other down to the left. Push both blades up a little so they slant slightly upward.

3. Hold the helicopter up high and let go. How does it fly?

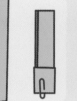

Fold the long strip like this.

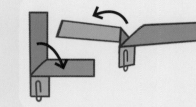

The simple strip helicopter does not fly quite as well because the wings are narrower. So less air pushes up against them and it falls faster.

331 Stiffer blades

Follow the instructions for activity 329 or 330 to make another helicopter the same size, but using card stock. Compare how the card stock and paper helicopters fly.

The card stock helicopter falls to the ground a little faster because it is heavier than the paper helicopter, but has the same amount of air pushing up against it.

With the blades folded like this, the helicopter spins clockwise.

With the blades folded like this, the helicopter spins counterclockwise.

332 Spinning direction

Release a helicopter and see which way it spins. Then, fold each blade the other way and watch how it spins this time.

The direction of spin depends on the position of the blades. When you fold the blades the other way, the helicopter will spin in the opposite direction.

333 No blades

Fold a long strip of paper in half. Fold up the folded end a little and add a paper clip. Hold it up high and let go. What happens?

The paper falls without spinning because there are no blades to push against the air.

You could see how many paper clips you can add, while still allowing the helicopter to fly.

334 Adding weight

Add more paper clips to a helicopter to increase the weight. What happens?

If there is too much weight, the downward pull becomes too strong and the helicopter falls without spinning.

Static electricity

See what happens when a force called static electricity builds up in objects, and find out how you can use it to move things.

335 Spooky static

1. Cut some ghost shapes out of tissue paper. Arrange them on a table or scatter them on the floor.

2. Rub a plastic ruler on a sweater for a couple of minutes.

3. Hold the ruler over the ghosts. Slowly bring it closer. What happens?

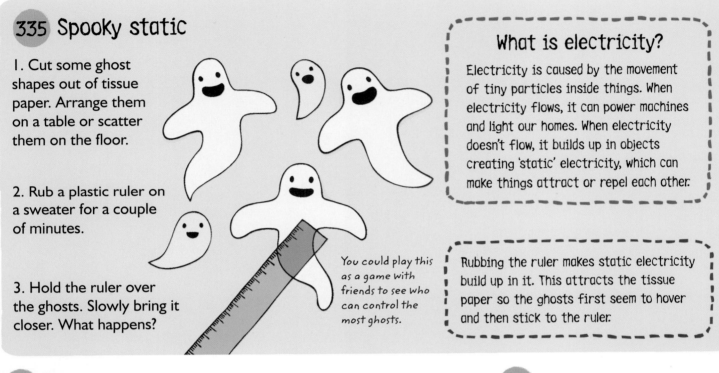

You could play this as a game with friends to see who can control the most ghosts.

What is electricity?

Electricity is caused by the movement of tiny particles inside things. When electricity flows, it can power machines and light our homes. When electricity doesn't flow, it builds up in objects creating 'static' electricity, which can make things attract or repel each other.

Rubbing the ruler makes static electricity build up in it. This attracts the tissue paper so the ghosts first seem to hover and then stick to the ruler.

336 Jumping pepper

1. Sprinkle a thin layer of ground pepper on the bottom of a clear plastic box and put on the lid.

2. Rub part of the lid with a scarf for a few minutes. What happens to the pepper? Rub all over the lid. What happens now?

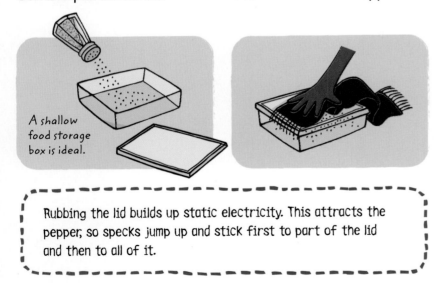

A shallow food storage box is ideal.

Rubbing the lid builds up static electricity. This attracts the pepper, so specks jump up and stick first to part of the lid and then to all of it.

337 Falling pepper

Repeat activity 336, then touch a paper clip to the lid of the box. What do you notice?

A plain metal paper clip works best.

The metal paper clip allows the electricity to flow away from the part of the lid it touches. There is no longer any static electricity to make the pepper stick there, so the specks fall down.

338 Electric hair

1. Rub a balloon against a carpet or sweater for a couple of minutes. Hold the balloon near someone's hair. What happens?

2. Now hold the balloon up to a wall. Let go. What happens?

Rubbing the balloon makes static electricity build up inside it.

The balloon will lift up your hair and stick to the wall. This is because things that have a build-up of static electricity are attracted to things that don't.

339 Bending water

1. Rub a plastic ruler on a sweater for a minute or two.

2. Turn on a faucet so you have a thin stream of water. Hold the ruler near the flow of water. What do you notice?

The static electricity in the ruler attracts the water, making it bend slightly toward the ruler.

340 Rolling can

1. Run a plastic comb through your hair a few times. Put an empty aluminum drink can on the ground.

2. Hold the comb near the can, then slowly pull it away. What happens?

Don't let the comb touch the can.

Combing makes static electricity build up in the comb, which then pulls the can toward it.

341 Bouncing balloons

1. Take two balloons and tie one of them to the back of a chair like this, so it hangs freely.

2. Rub both balloons against a sweater or your hair for a minute or two. Now try to bring the loose balloon near the tied one. What happens?

The balloons push each other away. That's because when two things have a lot of static electricty, they repel each other.

Right- and left-handed

Most people find it easier to do things with their right hands, but some prefer their left hands. A few people are equally good with both hands, or use different hands for different tasks. Try these experiments to find out more...

Brain control

Your brain has a right and a left side. The right side controls movements on the left of the body, and the left side controls movements on the right of the body.

The right side of the brain makes the left arm wave.

The left side of the brain makes the right leg move.

Nobody is entirely sure what makes people better at using one side or the other, but scientists do know that it often runs in families.

342 Writing

Using your right hand, write your name on a piece of paper. Now try it again using your left hand. Which do you find easier?

Most people write better with their right hand, and are known as right-handed. Some people write better with their left hand, and are described as left-handed. A few, rare people can write just as well with either hand. This is called being ambidextrous.

343 Throwing and catching

Throw a ball back and forth with a friend. Try throwing and catching with your left and right hand. Which do you find easier?

If you are right-handed, you will probably throw and catch best with your right hand, and vice versa if you are left-handed. But quite a few people prefer to throw and catch with a different hand from the one they write with.

Things that turn

Objects that need turning, such as can openers and corkscrews, are usually designed for right-handed people, who tend to turn things clockwise. Left-handed people tend to turn things counterclockwise, so find it easier to use left-handed versions which turn the other way.

344 Right- or left-handed shading

1. Draw a box with a pencil on paper. ----->

2. Ask a friend to use either hand to shade the box with diagonal lines, while you look away.

3. Look at the box once he or she has finished. Can you tell which hand your friend used?

People tend to shade in different directions, depending on which hand they are using.

If the lines are shaded like this, your friend probably used his or her right hand.

If they are shaded like this, your friend probably used his or her left hand.

345 Winking

Try winking with your right eye, then with your left eye. Can you do both?

Most people can wink with both eyes, but many are better winking on one side than the other. You might be able to improve your weaker side with practice, as the muscles in your face will get stronger.

346 Right- or left-footed?

1. Kick a ball at a goal with your right foot, then with your left foot. Which gives you more control?

2. Run a few steps and take a jump forward. Which leg do you leap off?

3. Walk up some stairs. Which foot do you lead with?

You may find you tend to do more with one foot than the other – and your best foot might be on the opposite side to your best hand. You can be 'right-handed' and 'left-footed' at the same time.

Growing crystals

These experiments will show you different ways to make dazzling crystals.

It can be tricky to grow crystals, especially in very hot, cold or damp weather, so you may need to try these experiments more than once.

347 Sugar crystals

1. Pour half a cup of just-boiled water into a pitcher. Add one cup of sugar and stir it until the sugar dissolves.

2. Pour the mixture into a jar. Dip a wooden skewer into the warm mixture, sprinkle the wet end with sugar and leave it to dry.

Don't let the skewer touch the jar, or the solution will rub off the stick and the crystals won't grow.

3. Once the mixture is cool, attach a clothespin to the clean end of the skewer and balance it on the jar, so the sugary end is in the mixture.

4. Leave the jar in a warm place. After a few days, the skewer should be covered in sugar crystals. You can eat them like lollipops, if you like.

When water is very hot, it can hold more dissolved sugar than when it is cold. When it cools down, the sugar comes out of the water and forms crystals on the skewer.

348 Bright lollipops

Try making more sugar crystals, this time stirring several drops of food dye into the water along with the sugar. You should get colorful crystal lollipops, like the ones on the right.

122

349 Alum crystals

Alum crystals

You can color your alum crystals by adding food dye to the hot water in step 1.

1. Mix half a cup of hot water with three tablespoons of alum* in a jar.

Cover the jar with a paper towel to keep out dust.

2. Leave the jar for a day or two until you can see small crystals forming at the bottom.

3. Use a sieve to separate the crystals from the liquid, then pour the liquid back into the jar.

4. Take the biggest crystal and tie a piece of thread around it. Tie the other end of the thread onto a pencil.

5. Balance the pencil on the jar, so the crystal is hanging in the liquid. How big is the crystal after a week?

350 Epsom salt crystals

1. Mix half a cup of hot water with two tablespoons of Epsom salt* in a pitcher.

2. Pour two tablespoons of the mixture onto a plate.

3. Bend one end of a cotton pipe cleaner into a star shape and place it in the mixture. Check it after a couple of days – it should be covered in crystals.

351 Baking soda crystals

Follow the steps in activity 350, but using bakind soda instead of Epsom salt.

Alum, Epsom salt and baking soda all dissolve in water. As the water evaporates (turns to water vapor), it leaves them behind in the form of crystals. The longer you leave each experiment, the bigger the crystals will grow.

* You can buy alum in the kitchen spice isle of the grocery store, and Epsom salt at the pharmacy.

⚠ Epsom salt is not safe to eat. Wash your hands after touching the crystals.

How plants drink

Here you can change the color of flowers and discover how plants take up water.

352 Make dyed flowers

1. Take a white gerbera or carnation. Remove any leaves, then leave it out of water for an hour.

2. Pour some water into a glass. Add two teaspoons of food dye and mix it in.

Cut the stem at an angle.

3. Trim the end of the flower stem. Then, put the flower in the dyed water.

4. Leave the flower for a day. How does it look?

Carnations and gerberas work well because they soak up lots of water.

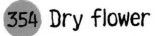

Gerbera

Yellow food dye in water

Carnation

353 Tubes

Use the flower from activity 352. Once its petals have changed color, cut across the stem. Can you see some little colored dots?

The flower petals should have changed color. Plant stems have narrow tubes inside that draw up the dyed water into the petals. The colored dots inside a stem are the ends of these tubes.

354 Dry flower

Leave a flower out of water for several hours. What happens to it?

Plants need water to stay healthy. Without it, cut flowers wilt (droop) and die.

Water and blue food dye

355 Bright flower

You will probably not see much change, if any at all. Two teaspoons of food dye isn't enough to show up against very bright petals, unlike white flowers. You might see some color if you add a lot more dye.

Take a flower with brightly colored petals and place it in dyed water. What happens?

356 Mix it up

Try dying other kinds of white flowers. How well do they work?

Some flowers, such as lilies, take up less water than others — so they will also take up less dye.

Lily

357 Flower race

1. Take two similar white flowers. Trim one, leaving a long stem. Cut the other stem short.

2. Leave both flowers in the same glass of dyed water. Check every half hour. Which petals start to change first?

The flower with the shorter stem changes first. This is because the dyed water has less far to travel to reach the petals.

358 Dying vegetables

You could also try dying vegetable leaves, such as cabbage or bok choy, or a stalk of celery.

Vegetable stems and leaves have tubes inside them, just like flower stems. The dyed water is drawn up the tubes and makes the leaves change color.

This bok choy leaf was left in blue water.

Parachutes

Make your own parachutes and find out how they work using a force known as air resistance.

359 Make a plastic parachute

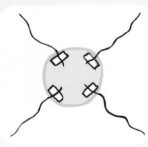

1. Place a large bowl on a plastic bag, draw around it and cut out a circle. Cut four pieces of string, about as long as your arm.

2. Arrange the pieces of string evenly around the circle and tape them on, like this.

Make sure the knot and clothespin hang in the middle.

3. Knot the ends of the strings together and attach a clothespin to the ends. Hold the parachute up high, let it go and watch how it falls.

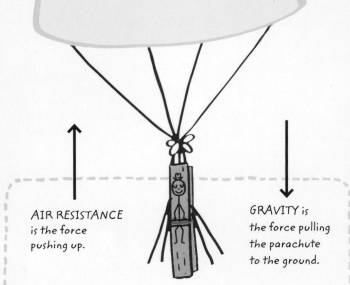

AIR RESISTANCE is the force pushing up.

GRAVITY is the force pulling the parachute to the ground.

As the parachute falls, it spreads out and traps air underneath it. This air pushes up against the parachute from below, creating a force known as air resistance. This slows the fall of the parachute.

360 Paper parachute

Using the method described in activity 359, make another parachute out of tissue paper.

A tissue–paper parachute falls in a similar way. The paper traps air, which slows the parachute's fall to the ground.

361 Small parachute

Use a smaller bowl to make smaller plastic and paper parachutes. See how they fall compared with the bigger parachutes from activities 359 and 360.

A smaller parachute creates less air resistance and falls more quickly.

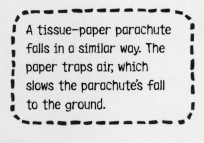

126

362 Square parachute

Make a square parachute out of paper or plastic. How does it compare to a round one?

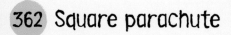

A square parachute falls in a similar way. Parachutes can be made in many different shapes, as long as they trap enough air.

363 No clothespin

Remove the clothespin from one of your parachutes and test it out again.

Without a clothespin, the parachute doesn't fall as smoothly. It needs some weight to keep it stable and upright.

364 Holey parachute

Use a sharp pencil to make several holes in a parachute. How quickly does it fall now?

A parachute with holes falls faster because it doesn't trap as much air.

365 Fabric parachute

Take an old handkerchief or dish towel and tie a string around each corner to make a fabric parachute. Test it out.

You can make a parachute from any light material. Fabric parachutes fall faster than plastic or paper ones because tiny holes in the fabric allow air through, and so reduce air resistance.

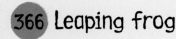

(366) Leaping frog

1. Draw a frog on paper and cut it out. Tape it to the side of a plastic cup.

2. Stretch two rubber bands around a plastic bowl.

3. Press the cup down on the bowl, then let go. Watch it jump.

As you press down, the rubber bands stretch and store up energy. When you let go, the energy is released, pushing the frog into the air.

Index

Edited by Rosie Dickins, Jane Chisholm and Kirsteen Robson; American editor: Carrie A. Armstrong;
Additional design & illustration: Sam Chandler and Erica Harrison; Photography by Howard Allman;
Additional photography: p.18 © Buena Vista Images/Getty Images; p.47 © D. Hurst/Alamy; p.55 © Joseph Clark/Getty Images; p.73 © Radius Images/Alamy;
p.79 © Ocean/Corbis; p.90 © Bon Appetit/Alamy.

Usborne Publishing is not responsible and does not accept liability for the availability or content of any website other than its own,
or for any exposure to harmful, offensive or inaccurate material which may appear on the Web. Usborne Publishing will have no liability
for any damage or loss caused by viruses that may be downloaded as a result of browsing the sites it recommends.

First published in 2014 by Usborne Publishing Ltd., Usborne House, 83–85 Saffron Hill, London, EC1N 8RT, United Kingdom. www.usborne.com
Copyright © 2014 Usborne Publishing Ltd. The name Usborne and the devices ♀⊕ are Trade Marks of Usborne Publishing Ltd. All rights reserved.
No part of this publication may be reproduced, stored in any retrieval system, or transmitted in any form or by any means, electronic, mechanical, photocopying,
recording or otherwise, without the prior permission of the publisher. AE. First published in America 2015.